KU-560-504

)server's Books

URAL HISTORY

· Birds' Eggs · Wild Animals · Zoo Animals
Animals · Freshwater Fishes · Sea Fishes
ical Fishes · Butterflies · Larger Moths
s and Spiders · Pond Life · Sea and Seashore
ells · Dogs · Horses and Ponies · Cats
· Wild Flowers · Grasses · Mushrooms · Lichens
· Garden Flowers · Flowering Shrubs
Plants · Vegetables · Geology · Weather
omy

T

ation Football · Cricket · Golf · Coarse Fishing
ing · Show Jumping · Motor Sport

PORT

biles · Aircraft · Commercial Vehicles
ycles · Steam Locomotives · Ships
raft · Manned Spaceflight · Unmanned Spacefli

TECTURE

ture · Churches · Cathedrals

TING

nd Medals · Coins · Postage Stamps · Glass
nd Porcelain

ND CRAFTS

ainting · Modern Art · Sculpture
· Sewing

AND GENERAL INTEREST

ritain · Flags · Heraldry · European Costume

Tourist Atlas GB

O

The Observer's Pocket Se

SEASHELLS OF THE BRIT

The Observer's Book of

SEASHELLS
OF THE BRITISH ISLES

NORA F. McMILLAN

WITH 195 LINE DRAWINGS BY
BRIDGET FINLOW AND 8 COLOUR
PLATES BY JOHN CLEGG

FREDERICK WARNE
LONDON

Published by
Frederick Warne (Publishers) Ltd
London, England
© Frederick Warne & Co Ltd 1977

ISBN 0 7232 15677

Text set in 9/10 pt Photon Baskerville,
printed by photolithography, and bound
in Great Britain at The Pitman Press, Bath

PREFACE

Most of us, at some time or another, have walked along the seashore and gathered shells. Afterwards we have wondered how to identify them and find out more about the living creatures that constructed the shells.

Seashells are, of course, merely the exterior skeletons of molluscs, and the collector ought not to be content with just gathering empty shells. Even the commonest living mollusc (e.g., a Periwinkle or Cockle) if placed in a suitable container of clean seawater (*not* in sunlight) and watched affords endless interest in its way of moving, feeding, etc. Much still remains to be learnt of the habits and habitats of molluscs.

Most molluscs are not difficult to identify from their shells, though beachworn specimens often present problems. With the present upsurge of shell-collecting there are many books available dealing with the showy tropical species, but there seems to be room for a small book to help identify some of the commoner seashells likely to be encountered around these islands. It is hopeful that this Observer's book will meet the need and encourage readers to look more carefully at molluscs in general.

Almost all the species described in this book can be recognized at sight or with a hand-lens at most.

5

For more detailed work on critical species a microscope is sometimes necessary, and reference to more advanced books essential. A list of helpful books will be found on pp. 151–2.

In the descriptions of the species the measurements given are those of average specimens. Dwarfs and giants can be found in most species. Care has been taken to set out clearly the differences between closely-allied species.

The fine colour-plates are from transparencies by John Clegg FRPS and the line-drawings are by Bridget Finlow. I am grateful to both for their patience with my demands.

Nora F. McMillan

CONTENTS

LIST OF COLOUR PLATES

GLOSSARY

Adductor muscle scars Depressions (1 or 2) on the inside of bivalves showing attachment areas of adductor muscles which hold the two valves together. Important for identification. *See* Fig. 1.

Aperture The opening of gastropod shells. The 'mouth' of some older books. *See* Fig. 2.

Apical (of whorls) Those at the tip of a gastropod shell.

Auricle The ear-like projection of a *Teredo* shell.

Apophysis The strip-like projection beneath the beak within pholad valves (piddocks).

Beak Tip of a valve, usually pointed. *See* Fig. 1.

Bivalve A mollusc with a 2-valved shell, e.g., cockle.

Bodywhorl The last and lowest whorl of a gastropod shell.

Byssus Bundle of fibres secreted by the animal and used as a mooring-rope, e.g., mussel.

Canal A narrow groove or spout-like prolongation of the aperture in some gastropod shells.

Cephalopods The cuttles, octopus and squids.

Chitons Small group of molluscs with a shell composed of 8 shelly plates.

Chondrophore The ligament-pit (q.v.).

Dextral   Gastropod shell with a right-hand 'twist'; when shell is held with spire upwards and aperture towards observer the aperture is on the right. Most gastropods are dextral.

Ears   The lateral projections on each side of the beak in scallops.

Epidermis   An older name for periostracum (q.v.).

Gastropod   Mollusc with a single, usually spiral shell. In some species e.g., limpets, the spiral has been lost.

Girdle   The fleshy tissue surrounding and holding together the eight valves of chitons. Important for identification.

Head-scar   Markings inside the apex of a limpet shell, showing position of muscle. Colour important for identification.

Imperforate   Without umbilicus.

Lamellibranch   Mollusc with a 2-valved shell, e.g., cockle. Another name for a bivalve is pelecypod.

Ligament   The fibrous band which hinges the two valves of bivalve shells.

Ligament-pit (chondrophore)   The socket to which the ligament is attached. Sometimes it is a prominent projection as in *Mya*.

Loricate   Chitons (q.v.).

Lunule   A depressed area present in some bivalves in front of the beaks, usually differing in sculpture or colouring from the rest of the shell.

LWNT   Low water of neap tides.

LWST   Low water of spring tides.

LWEST   Low water of equinoctial spring tides.

Pallial line   The mark on the inside of a bivalve, indicating where the mantle lobes were situated, parallel to the lower margin and connecting the two adductor muscles. *See* Fig. 1.

Pallial sinus   An indentation in the pallial line, opening towards the posterior end of the valve.

Pelagic   Living in the open sea, floating.

Periphery   The widest part of a whorl.

Peristome   The rim of the aperture of a gastropod shell, the 'lip'.

Plankton   Very small animals which live drifting in the sea. Includes larval stages of many molluscs.

Protoconch   The embryonic whorls at the tip of a gastropod shell.

Radula   The dental apparatus of a gastropod mollusc; a ribbon-like structure bearing teeth and used to rasp off small particles of organic matter. Important for identification.

Scaphopods   Tusk-shells (*Dentalium* spp.).

Sinistral   Left-handed. When gastropod shell is held with the spire upwards and aperture facing observer, aperture is to left.

sp   Abbreviation for species. Plural is 'spp.' (species).

11

Suture   Line formed by junction of whorls in a gastropod shell.

Umbilicus   A central navel-like depression on the underside of the bodywhorl of a gastropod shell; the central hollow cavity of the columella.

Umbo (singular) **umbones** (plural)   The part of a valve just behind the beaks. Often used to describe the beaks.

Varix   A thickened rib; noticeably thicker than its fellows.

Whorl   The visible part of a single coil of a gastropod shell.

To distinguish between the right and left valves of a bivalve

If the specimen is complete, hold it with the beaks uppermost so that the ligament is between you and the beaks, which usually turn away from you. The right and left valves of the mollusc will then correspond to your right and left. If there is a pallial sinus this should open towards you, and if there is only one adductor muscle scar it should be on the nearer half of the valve.

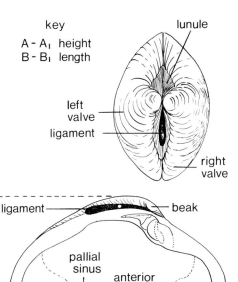

key

A - A₁ height
B - B₁ length

lunule

left valve

ligament

right valve

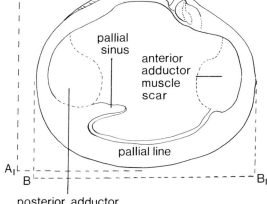

A

ligament

beak

pallial sinus

anterior adductor muscle scar

pallial line

A₁

B

B₁

posterior adductor muscle scar

Fig. 1. Diagram showing the parts of a bivalve shell

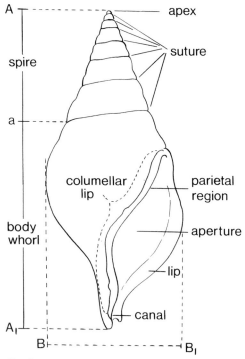

key

| A A_1 - height | a - A_1 body whorl |
| A a - spire | B - B_1 breadth |

Fig. 2. Diagram showing the parts of a gastropod shell

INTRODUCTION

There are about 600 species of Mollusca living in the seas around the British Isles. Many of these live on the seashore or in shallow water and it is these that the beginner is most likely to encounter. About 200 species are described in this book and over 150 illustrated, some in colour. Of the remaining 400 or so species some live only in deep water (but examples may sometimes be cast up on shores after storms) and some are so tiny that a microscope is necessary for their study. In some species the shell is internal and in some, notably the beautiful sea-slugs, there is no shell at all.

The Mollusca are divided into the following classes:

MONOPLACOPHORA   No British species.

AMPHINEURA   The chitons or coat-of-mail shells, and a few worm-like shell-less species.

GASTROPODA   Comprise about three-quarters of all known molluscs. Divided into three sub-classes.

(i) sub-class *PROSOBRANCHIA* (gill-breathing) Almost all marine, it includes limpets, winkles and whelks.

(ii) sub-class *OPISTHOBRANCHIA* All marine except one family. Includes the bubble-shells, sea-butterflies (pteropods) and sea-slugs.

(iii) sub-class *PULMONATA* (lung-breathing) Practically all land and fresh-water species.

SCAPHOPODA   The small group of the tusk-shells.

LAMELLIBRANCHIA   A large group of species with a 2-valved shell: examples are mussel, oyster, cockle.

CEPHALOPODA   The most highly-developed group. Includes the tropical Pearly Nautilus with its external shell, squids and cuttles with internal shells and octopods with no shells.

HOW TO FIND SHELLS

Seashells are easy to find, and every available piece of coastline should be searched. Rocky shores with plenty of pools between high and low water mark provide many species. Limpets and chitons adhere to rock-faces, winkles live in crevices, and many small gastropods live in seaweeds. Further down the shore are the big brown kelps or oarweeds (*Laminaria* spp)., and this part of the shore is the richest of all. Search the "fronds" of the *Laminaria* for Blue-rayed Limpets and chink-shells etc., look at the rock to which the oarweeds are attached, and then turn over any largish stones and examine carefully the undersides. Be sure to turn the stones back again afterwards!

Sandy shores often yield a rich harvest of empty shells but only occasionally, usually after gales, are many living specimens found. Digging is often necessary to obtain living examples of the various sand-living bivalves.

Estuaries, brackish lagoons, and salt-marshes all harbour mud-loving molluscs and should not be neglected.

The best time for collecting living molluscs is when the tide is furthest out and during the period of spring tides when the difference between high and low water is greatest. Spring tides occur at the time of the new moon and the full moon and the times of high and low tides can be ascertained from a local tide-table, (a stationer's or an anglers' shop can usually supply one) or from the Admiralty Tide Tables (in any good Reference Library). The equinoctial spring tides in March and September are specially good as the maximum expanse of shore is then revealed. Try to get to the shore an hour or so before the time of low water and follow the falling tide out to its lowest ebb. Turn back at once as it begins to flow in again.

Although the richest part of the shore is that laid bare by spring tides yet those areas lying nearer to the High Water Mark (HWM) should not be overlooked. Some interesting species live near HWM, some, indeed, even higher up the shore in the well-named 'splash zone' where they are only reached by spray or very high tides. Look under stones, investigate sheltered corners, and do not neglect muddy tidal creeks or brackish lagoons. Handfuls of waterweeds or seaweeds left overnight in tap water often yield unsuspected species.

No elaborate collecting gear is needed; a bucket, some bags and tubes, all preferably of plastic, penknife, pencil and notebook, and a good hand-lens (slung on a cord around one's neck for safety). A spade and sieve are useful on a sandy or muddy shore.

Bulk samples of shellsand can be taken home, washed in fresh water and dried, then painstakingly sorted. This process often yields species not easily obtained otherwise.

WHERE TO GO

The western coastline of Europe extends from North Cape to Gibraltar, from the Arctic to the Mediterranean. Midway lie the islands of Britain and Ireland with an enormous length of the most varied coastline in Europe. It stretches from Unst, the northernmost of the Shetland Islands in the north to Alderney, the most southerly of the Channel Islands, six thousand miles of mainland coastline and very many hundreds of miles more when one includes Ireland and all the numerous islands satellite to both Britain and Ireland. Between Shetland and Alderney are cliffbound coasts, the long sheltered inlets of the sea in the far south-west, in south-west Ireland, and the west of Scotland, wide sandy bays, shingle beaches, bars and spits, estuaries and stretches of salt-marsh and mudflat. All these afford wonderful opportunities for finding and studying our Mollusca. We are fortunate in these islands that we have no need to make long journeys in search of molluscs.

There is no 'best place' for shell-collectors in Britain though the famous shell-beach at Herm (Channel Islands) approaches most nearly to that ideal.

If possible, always get a local conchologist to advise about good collecting-grounds and what to look for. He will know the local specialities! 'Local lists' of the shells of any one locality are most useful as a guide to what one may expect to find; a few are given below but the local library should be able to help with local conchological literature.

The following notes on some areas may be found

useful.

Channel Islands   Very rich in species and contain some species not found elsewhere in Britain. Have an enormous tidal range so great care is necessary to avoid being trapped by the incoming tide.

South-west (Devon, Cornwall and the Scilly Islands)   Also very rich especially the south coast. North coast rather poor in living molluscs. Mrs Turk's book *Seashore Life in Cornwall and the Isles of Scilly* (publ. Truro 1971) on pp. 24–25 maps Cornish coasts and those of Scilly with notes on habitats represented. *The Plymouth Marine Fauna*, 3rd Edn (1957) covers a much wider area than the title suggests. Write to The Director, the Laboratory, Citadel Hill, Plymouth.

South coast   Dorset is fairly rich but to eastward collecting becomes progressively poorer.

East coast   The whole east coast from Essex north to Caithness is much less rich in number of species than the west but nevertheless some good species are to be found (usually dredged, unfortunately) in the North Sea. There is a good list of Mollusca in *The Natural History of Scarborough District*, Vol. 2 Zoology (1956) edited by G. B. Walsh and F. C. Rimington. For eastern Scotland there is an up-to-date list of Mollusca in *Fauna and Flora of St Andrews Bay*, Eds M. S. Laverack and M. C. H. Blackler (publ. Scottish Academic Press, 1974).

North coast (Scotland)   The group of Orkney Islands affords excellent shore-collecting. A good molluscan guide is R. Rendall's *Mollusca Orcadensia*. This was published by the Royal Society of Edinburgh in their *Proceedings* (Vol. 56, B, no. 7, 1956) but separate copies are sometimes obtainable.

West coast Some species characteristic of the south-west extend right up the west coast as far as Orkney but the number lessens as one goes north. Many rare species occur on the west coast of Scotland, and Oban is a good centre. The following lists are all good: J. A. Allen *The Fauna of the Clyde Sea Area. Mollusca* (1962) (publ. by the Scottish Marine Biological Association—write to The Librarian, Marine Station, Millport, Isle of Cumbrae, Scotland); for the Isle of Man there is the *Marine Fauna of the Isle of Man and its surrounding Seas* (1963) by J. R. Bruce, J. S. Coleman and N. S. Jones—write to the Marine Biological Station, Port Erin, Isle of Man; for south-west Wales there is a good list in *Dale Fort Marine Fauna*, 2nd Edn, Ed. J. H. Crothers—write to E. W. Classey Ltd, Park Road, Faringdon, OXON SN7 7DR.

Ireland Good collecting almost everywhere because, generally speaking, beaches are clean. The far south-west (Co. Kerry) is particularly good and so are the well-known Velvet Strand of Portmarnock, Co. Dublin and Magilligan Strand, Co. Londonderry (Northern Ireland).

Finally **do not collect large numbers**, except of the very commonest species. Over-collecting can ruin the most prolific of beaches.

Alien molluscs occasionally reach our shores alive

and some have become established and breed here. Such are the Slipper Limpet (*Crepidula fornicata*) and the American tingle (*Urosalpinx cinerea*) both North American natives accidentally introduced with American oysters and both now serious pests of our native oyster. The tingle preys on our oysters, the slipper limpets compete with them for food.

Another but harmless import is the American piddock (*Petricola pholadiformis*) which is not a piddock at all but a boring mollusc allied to the Venus shells. Yet another North American import is the highly edible Quahog or Hardshell Clam (*Mercenaria mercenaria*) now flourishing in several places in southern England. It has also been deliberately introduced in Ireland (south coast).

Oceanic waifs such as the Violet Snail (*Janthina janthina*) and the coiled pearly shell (internal) of the cephalopod *Spirula peronii* are sometimes drifted to our shores but very seldom alive.

Such oddments as the Florida tree snails found on a Cornish beach, the Indian Ocean olive-shell picked up in Shetland and the Pacific Vase-shell from the South Lancs. coast are obviously the result of spring-cleaning operations!

PREPARING SHELLS FOR YOUR COLLECTION

To prepare shells for your collection wash in warm water but do not remove the outer fibrous covering (the periostracum) present on some. To kill live specimens drop into fast-boiling water and boil for a few minutes; bivalves will then gape open and the soft parts can be removed. Tie the valves together with soft thread at once so that they will remain closed when dry; it is a good idea to keep one or two specimens with the valves open so that the interior can be seen as this is often necessary for identification. Use a pin or fine hook (a bent needle is handy) to pull out the soft parts from gastropod shells, saving the operculum—the little 'door' which closes the aperture of the shell in many species (though not all gastropods have opercula). This should be dried and kept with the shell; some collectors plug the aperture of the shell with cotton wool and gum the operculum on in the position of life. Chitons should be eased off with a knife, transferred to a slip of wood and bound in their natural flat position for a couple of weeks until quite dry and 'set'.

Very small molluscs (shells less than 5 mm long) need not be cleaned. Place in spirit (methylated will do but industrial is much better) for a few weeks, then allow to dry on blotting-paper 48 hours before storing.

HOUSING YOUR COLLECTION

This is a matter of personal preference. Cabinets are nice but very expensive, though secondhand ones are sometimes to be obtained reasonably. Largish shells can be housed adequately in plastic bags, smaller ones in match-boxes, neatly covered with white paper, or in glass tubes.

Labels These are important for the finest specimen loses much of its scientific value if it has no data. So label your shells with full data (locality, date, collector's name, and if possible kind of habitat where obtained). Thus: *Mya arenaria* L. Marine Lake, West Kirby, Cheshire, 17.iii.1974. In muddy sand. Coll. J. Bull.

It is a wise precaution to use Roman numerals for the month instead of Arabic, as Americans often put the month first and confusion could arise if both numbers were Arabic. Thus, use 17.iii.1974 in preference to 17.3.1974.

Use pencil for field-notes and labels, but Indian ink for permanent labels. Some collectors number their shells in Indian ink and keep the relevant information under that number in a record-book but sometimes the record-book and collection become separated and then the shells are almost valueless. Gastropods that are sufficiently large can have the label tucked into the aperture, and with large bivalves data can be inscribed on the inside of a valve (use Indian ink).

THE NAMES OF SHELLS

Seashells, unlike birds and butterflies, usually have no common or English names. There are, of course, a few exceptions such as cockle, mussel, oyster, scallop, whelk and winkle, but even these names are each applied to more than one species. In this book, therefore, there is little consistency in the English names used. Where there is a fairly well-known name, such as scallop or mussel, then it has been used but often there is none and in these cases the scientific name has had to be used. In any case we all happily use scientific ('Latin') names for our garden plants so why not for shells?

A scientific name consists of three words, firstly the genus (plural genera) which is a group of closely-allied animals, secondly the species or one particular kind of animal, and finally the name of the author who first made known that special species. For example, many whelks are of the genus *Buccinum* but only our familiar whelkstall delicacy is *Buccinum undatum* Linné. Linné is Carl von Linné, sometimes Latinized to Carolus Linnaeus, the Swedish genius who in 1758 produced his scheme in which for the first time animals were each given a short name of two words only (as in our example *Buccinum undatum*) instead of the long and cumbersome descriptive names previously used. So all the scientific names of animals date from 1758, all earlier names being ignored. Many later authors have described species that Linné did not and their names similarly follow the species they described.

Above genera come families, gathering related genera into larger groups; families in turn are arranged into orders and above these are the great classes or sub-classes of the phylum Mollusca.

Our whelk is therefore classified thus:

Phylum MOLLUSCA
Class GASTROPODA
Sub-class PROSOBRANCHIA
Order STENOGLOSSA
Family Buccinidae
Genus *Buccinum*
Species *undatum* L.

(Note: Linné is often abbreviated to L.)

A useful convention is that when the same species is referred to more than once fairly close together then the name is given in full the first time and thereafter only the initial letter of the generic name is used. Thus our example *Buccinum undatum* Linné becomes *B. undatum* L.

For those who wish to pursue the matter of scientific names further *Naming the Living World* by Theodore Savory (English Universities Press, 1962) is an excellent introduction to the principles of biological nomenclature.

HISTORY OF BRITISH SHELL-COLLECTING

There have always been people who collected and delighted in shells. In early days 'curiosities' (which included exotic shells) were much prized and wealthy collectors vied with one another in filling their elegant cabinets with 'natural curiosities'. Martin Lister (1638–1712) may be truly described as the Father of British conchology for in his book *Historiae Animalium Angliae* (1678) he gives much information of British shells, both seashells and those of the land and freshwater. In the eighteenth and nineteenth centuries come most of the great names in British conchology. Emanuel Mendez da Costa (1717–1791) who wrote a conchological best-seller of his time; his other conchological venture came to an untimely end owing to the author's incarceration in gaol! The Welshman Thomas Pennant (1726–1798) lived all his life in Whiteford, Flintshire, and produced a useful *British Zoology* in four volumes; the volume containing the Mollusca appeared in 1777. In 1913 his collection of shells which had lain undisturbed since his death in 1798 was given to the Natural History Museum. Colonel George Montagu (1753–1815) scoured the south Devon shores and added many species to the British list, Dr William Turton (1762–1835) accepted, perhaps too readily, alien species purporting to be British, the gifted Edward Forbes (1814–1854) who after a brilliant career died at the early age of 39, and Sylvanus Hanley (1819–1899) a wealthy amateur who collaborated with Forbes to produce the still-indispensable 4 volume *History of British Mollusca and their Shells*. Finally there was the great John Gwyn Jeffreys (1809–1885), a lawyer, who wrote the equally-indispensable 5 volume *British Conchology*. And very many more, too numerous to mention, have contributed in greater or lesser degree to knowledge of our British shells and their makers.

(A list of helpful books will be found at the end of this volume). Today the emphasis is mainly on the living animal, its anatomy, physiology, behaviour and relation to its environment. Here the amateur can help materially for we have only begun to explore the relations of molluscs to other animals and plants and to the physical surroundings.

SEASHELLS AND ARCHAEOLOGY

Ancient man enjoyed eating shellfish as much as many of us do today, and archaeological sites often yield quantities of seashells. The species represented naturally vary according to what was available in the immediate neighbourhood; species commonly found are cockle, mussel, oyster, limpet, winkle and whelk. Sometimes razorshells (*Ensis* species) and other species are also present and the assemblage gives us a glimpse of the fauna of those times. For instance, the Iron Age kitchen-midden at Jarlshof in Shetland contained large numbers of winkles (*Littorina littorea*) and limpets (*Patella vulgata*), but only a few cockles, mussels and razorshells.

The Romans were especially fond of oysters and large quantities of oyster shells are found on Roman sites in Britain. An elegant example of how a knowledge of seashells can detect an archaeological fraud was the finding of a decorated shell of the American Blue Point Oyster (*Crassostrea virginica*) among a series of objects (including other decorated oyster shells) alleged to have been obtained from ancient pile-dwellings on the Clyde; American oysters were not imported into Britain until the nineteenth century!

Rarely, exotic shells are found; an Indian Ocean cowry in a prehistoric grave in Hampshire and two Red Sea cowries in Saxon graves in Kent, but these must have been highly valued, probably for their association with fertility in women. A prehistoric site on Oronsay, Inner Hebrides, contained a necklace of our little British cowries (*Trivia* spp) and these shells are still regarded as 'lucky' today; this is probably the last dim flicker of the fertility tradition.

In more recent times shells have served a variety of purposes in folk-life. Scottish crofters made a serviceable lamp out of a 'buckie', usually *Neptunea antiqua*, suspended horizontally with a wick lying in the canal of the shell. Large bivalves served as scoops for meal and flour, the deep valves of the big scallop (*Pecten maximus*) make good scoops, pie-dishes, ladles, and so on. Many species were utilized for bait in fishing communities, and were often gathered for pigs and fowl as well as for human consumption.

In Iceland, Norway, Shetland and Orkney children play farm-games on the shore, with different shells representing horses, cattle, sheep and a sheep-dog. Sheep were always represented by a cockle of some sort, the ribbed corrugations on the shell suggesting the sheep's fleece. In Norway verisimilitude was carried further, for as all bivalves have two shells (i.e. valves) these naturally represented male and female animals, the right valve being male, the left female. But as a farm stock should consist mainly of females, most of the bulls and rams had to be slaughtered—by smashing the right valves with a stone.

Apart from shells being used by children as toys they are much used as ornaments. Wentletraps (*Clathrus* spp.) mounted in silver make charming earrings, various species are strung for necklaces and 'shellcraft' is quite largely practised in making ornaments, ash-trays and so on for the tourist trade. Some shell-pictures or collages are really beautiful in their artistic use of shells, though often many tropical species are employed as being more colourful.

MOLLUSCS AS FOOD

Nowadays relatively few species of Mollusca are eaten in Britain compared with Mediterranean diets.

Oysters (at a price!), cockles, mussels, scallops, winkles and whelks are usual; spoots or razorfish (*Ensis* spp.) and limpets occasionally. *Mya arenaria*, the esteemed softshell clam of the USA but variously known as gaper, old maid or brallion in Great Britain, is sometimes eaten as is also the allied *Mya truncata*, called Smurslin in Shetland. The Ormer (*Haliotis tuberculata*) is a delicacy in the Channel Islands where the Warty Venus (*Venus verrucosa*) is also eaten; the big Spiny Cockle (*Cardium aculeatum*) of the south Devon coast and a few other species are sampled occasionally. In many places the large Horse mussel (*Modiolus modiolus*) is used for bait only but in Glasgow these molluscs are called Clabbidoos (a corruption of the Gaelic *Claba-dubha*, literally 'black, large-mouth'), are considered a delicacy and regularly offered for sale.

'Inkfish' (i.e., squids and cuttlefish) are sold regularly in some places and command a small but dedicated clientele.

For many shellfish recipes using British species see Alan Davidson's book *Mediterranean Seafood* (Penguin Paperback, 1972; reprinted 1976.)

ABOUT MOLLUSCS

Their Shells

The shells of both gastropods and bivalves are constructed by special glands at the edge of the animal's mantle. These deposit layers of shelly material, forms of calcium carbonate, and varying in structure and composition from family to family of molluscs.

Some shells have a thickened rib (varix) at the edge

of the lip (peristome) and this represents a period when no growth was made. Likewise the 'teeth' sometimes seen within the outer lip of the Dog Whelk (*Nucella lapillus*) represent a resting period caused by food-shortage.

The colouring of a shell is determined by pigment-producing cells at the mantle edge. Professor Tucker Abbott has well described the process thus 'The ground colour is produced by the special activity of groups of cells, often sharply localized. Where the activity of these groups is cyclical, blotching results; where the activity spreads from a focus, there may be formed zig-zags, V-shaped or circle patterns'. If a shell has been damaged and subsequently repaired by the occupant the 'repair' is always uncoloured.

Food of Molluscs

Molluscs show a wide variety of feeding habits and of food consumed. Many marine gastropods are carnivorous and actively hunt their living prey, some feed on carrion, some graze on seaweeds, and some feed on detritus of various kinds.

The neat round holes so often found in bivalve shells are usually the work of Necklace-shells (*Natica* spp.) who plough through the sandy beaches in search of the bivalves upon which they feed. Having found a suitable victim the snail presses its proboscis against the bivalve, usually about the middle of the shell, and an acid secreted by a gland on the underside of the proboscis gradually erodes the substance of the shell into a hole through which the victim's tissues are then extracted. Holes made by *Natica* spp.

have bevelled sides, while those made by other carnivorous molluscs such as sting-winkles (*Ocenebra* spp.) and dog-whelks (*Nucella lapillus*) have straight sides and are excavated mechanically by the radula.

Other species (i.e., the Netted Dog whelk *Nassarius reticulatus*) are scavengers, quickly assembling from quite considerable distances to feed on carrion. Many species eat both carrion and live prey: the Whelk *Buccinum undatum* for example.

Our little cowries (*Trivia* spp.) feed on the jelly-like star-studded compound ascidians and also insert their vase-shaped egg-cases into the ascidian. Many of the bubble-shells and their kin (the Canoe-shell *Tricla lignaria* and the smaller species of *Cylichna* and *Retusa*) seize their living prey of bivalves, other gastropods and foraminifera, and then crush it in their gizzards which are armed with strong tooth plates.

The various species of *Eulima* with their highly-polished shells are parasites, associated with different sea-urchins and starfishes. The numerous species of Pyramid-shells are also parasitic sucking the blood of various other animals, bivalves, sea-urchins, worms and so on. Many of these molluscs are rarely encountered in a living state but this is probably because little is yet known of their habits or host-animals and we do not know just where to look for them. Once more is learnt of the ecology of such molluscs they may prove to be not uncommon.

Among the vegetarian molluscs are the limpets, top-shells and some winkles, all of which graze on seaweeds. And so, of course, do many other species including the curious coat-of-mail shells or chitons.

Tusk-shells (*Dentalium* spp.) have clusters of sticky

tentacles protruding from the larger (anterior) end of the shell; these search for and catch living foraminifera and sometimes very young bivalves. The prey is then hauled into the captor's mouth.

Bivalves can conveniently be divided into two groups so far as their feeding habits are concerned. Some are suspension feeders that pump water through their bodies and thus strain off anything edible. Suspension feeders include the scallops, oysters, cockles and venus-shells, and all have short siphons or none at all.

Deposit-feeders, on the other hand, such as the tellins (*Tellina* spp.) and gapers (*Mya* spp.) burrow more or less deeply but have long siphons with which they suck up food from the muddy bottom where they live. The wood-boring shipworms (*Teredo* spp.) live almost entirely upon a diet of cellulose derived from the wood-shavings upon which they feed.

The small group of basket-shells (*Cuspidaria* spp.) are unique among bivalves in that they are carnivorous, feeding mainly upon small dead crustaceans.

Breeding

Most marine gastropods are of separate sexes, i.e., either male or female. The female shell is often larger (sometimes much larger) and possesses a more capacious bodywhorl. In the Pale Chink-shell (*Lacuna pallidula*) for instance, the male is only about one-tenth of the size of the female and lives permanently attached to the shell of his large mate. In the little Jenkins' spire-shell (*Potamopyrgus jenkinsi*) which lives in brackish or fresh water only ONE male animal has ever been found; all other specimens have been female and reproduce parthenogenetically, that is, without needing a male. As this mollusc also produces living young and as only one specimen is necessary to start a colony it is excellently fitted for colonizing new waters. Its rapid spread throughout Europe after its first discovery in 1859 in the brackish waters of the Thames is proof of its pioneering ability.

The opisthobranch molluscs, which include the bubble-shells and the shell-less sea-slugs, are hermaphrodite and individuals function as both male and female. Sex-reversal is known in a few molluscs, notably in the American slipper-limpet (*Crepidula fornicata*) which begins life as a male then as it grows older and larger it assumes female attributes. It also possesses the curious habit of clambering on top of another slipper-limpet so that eventually a 'chain' of perhaps six or more individuals one on top of another is formed, the oldest at the base of the chain being aged females, the intermediate animal an intermediate form partaking of both sexes and then the younger and smaller males completing the chain.

Some gastropods produce living young, e.g., the Rough Winkle (*Littorina saxatilis*) but the majority lay eggs (spawn). In some cases (Limpets and top-shells) the eggs are discharged directly into the water but in many species the eggs are protected by special cases or capsules. Examples of the latter are whelks, buckies and dog-whelks. Others deposit eggs embedded in a jellylike substance, e.g., the Flat Winkle (*Littorina littoralis*) and the Chink-shells (*Lacuna* spp.), and some form a collar-like strip of eggs incorporated with sandgrains as in the

Necklace-shells (*Natica catena*) The Violet Snail (*Janthina britannica*) constructs a floating raft of a secretion from its foot and the egg-capsules are attached to the underside of this raft.

Many molluscan eggs hatch into a swimming larval form known as a veliger. Veligers swim by means of fringed lobes and often have larval shells quite different from those of the adult animals. In some species the swimming stage lasts only a few days or even hours, in others two or three months. Finally they drop to the bottom where they begin adult life, usually crawling.

It is possible to tell from the embryonic whorls (protoconch) at the tip of a gastropod shell whether it has had a short or a long larval life. A protoconch of several whorls with a small apex indicates a larva which has had a lengthy swimming stage; a simple protoconch with a large bulbous apex has had a brief swimming stage.

Many gastropods complete their development within the egg-capsule, the young emerging as miniatures of their parent and all ready for independent life. In some cases the egg-yolk provides enough food for development (e.g., Rough Winkle *Littorina saxatilis* and the Chink-shells *Lacuna* spp.) but frequently further provision for the young has been made in the form of nurse-eggs. These are eggs enclosed within the same capsule as the fertile eggs but which do not develop and upon which the developing young feed. Examples of this are found in the Whelk *Buccinum undatum* and the Dog whelk *Nucella lapillus*. When newly hatched the very young molluscs hide deep in crevices at first and are therefore seldom found.

Bivalves are mostly of separate sexes, although a few are true hermaphrodites and some indulge in change of sex. In fact our native oyster (*Ostrea edulis*) alternates its sex throughout its life!

Most bivalves spawn great numbers of eggs directly into the water and the larval stages have a long life of up to two or three months. In good years they settle in great numbers and hence the crop of adults varies widely from year to year. One need only think of mussels covering every available surface or of cockles forming a continuous layer just below the surface of a sandy bay to realize this.

Some female bivalves (e.g., *Lasaea rubra*) retain the fertilized eggs within their shells until the young are well developed and only then are they released. In such cases the number of young is of course small.

Length of Life

Little is known of the lifespan of marine molluscs except in the case of species of economic importance. Gapers (*Mya arenaria*) take about five years to reach full size (about 75–100 mm) and may live for ten years. The common mussel (*Mytilus edulis*) reaches a length of 50 mm in its first year and attains 100 mm in its second year, after which it grows very little although it may live for seven or eight years.

Oysters are not normally allowed to live out their lives naturally but they reach a size of 100 mm as adults. Occasionally solitary specimens are encountered living in deep water and these sometimes attain a great size, up to 160 × 130 mm, and are probably many years old. Such solitary specimens may weigh as much as 1·2 kg, most of this weight being the thick and heavy shell.

DETAILS OF INDIVIDUAL SHELLS
Chitons or Coat-of-Mail Shells

Chitons (Class AMPHINEURA) or coat-of-mail shells have boat-shaped shells composed of eight shelly plates or valves which lie across the animal's back and overlap each other, with a fleshy girdle around the edge. The granulations on the girdle are important for identification and a good hand-lens or microscope is necessary for their examination.

Chitons adhere to stones and old shells between tide-marks as well as in deeper water and there are a dozen British species. All are herbivorous and graze on seaweeds.

Lepidopleurus asellus (Gmelin) The commonest chiton below LWM and in dredgings. Usually yellowish, the girdle with delicate overlapping and rectangular scales. About 13 mm long and 8 mm wide. (Fig. 3.)

Lepidochitona cinereus (L.) The commonest inter-tidal chiton. Rather narrow and arched, surface of valves shagreened and variegated red-brown, yellow and green. The variegated girdle is closely and finely granulated. About 12 mm long. (Fig. 4.)

Tonicella marmorea (Fabricius) (Fig. 5). Our largest chiton, usually about 20–25 mm long, variegated red-brown and yellowish-white. Girdle is leathery, sparingly and minutely granulated. A northern species only occurring N of Yorkshire and Dublin. The allied *Tonicella rubra* (L.) is common, only half the size and the girdle is chequered red and white.

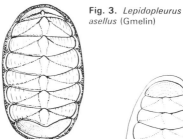

Fig. 3. *Lepidopleurus asellus* (Gmelin)

Fig. 4. *Lepidopleurus cinereus* (L.)

Fig. 5. *Tonicella marmorea* (Fabricus)

Fig. 6. *Acanthochitona crinitus* (Pennant)

The tufted chitons (3 species) bear tufts of bristles on the girdle.

Acanthochitona crinitus (Pennant) is the commonest species, about 13 mm long and with 18 tufts (Fig. 6). *A. discrepans* (Brown) is a little larger and has 19–20 tufts, found mostly in the SW.

Ormer or Ear-Shell and Limpets

The Ear-shell or Ormer and the limpets are the most lowly of the great class GASTROPODA and of the sub-class PROSOBRANCHIA (gill-breathing) of which there are nearly 200 marine representatives in Britain. Limpets, whelks and winkles are some of the most familiar species. In most cases the animal can withdraw into its shell, the aperture being then closed by an operculum, but this is not always the case. Limpets cannot emerge from the shell and have no operculum.

Ormer or ear-shell *Haliotis tuberculata* L. (*See* colour plate 1). Up to 90 mm long. The older holes in the shell become closed by shell-growth as newer holes are formed. Largely gathered for food in the Channel Islands where alone it occurs in Britain.

Slit limpet *Emarginula reticulata* (Sowerby) A white cancelled shell 6 mm long with 25–35 ribs crossed by slighter ribs. Common from LWST downwards (Fig. 7). The little Channel Island slit limpet (*E. conica* Lamarck) is smaller (5 mm), usually pinkish, and the long much incurved beak overhangs the front margin of the shell. The rare *E. crassa* (Sowerby) is much larger (up to 32 mm) with 40–50 ribs crossed by fine concentric striae. N and W Scotland in 10–40 m (20–75) fm, exceptionally at LWST.

Fig. 7. *Emarginula reticulata* (Sowerby)

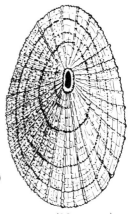

Fig. 8. *Diodora apertura* (Montagu)

Keyhole limpet *Diodora apertura* (Montagu) Yellow white with brown rays, 22 mm long. From LWM downwards, frequent. (Fig. 8.)

Common limpet *Patella vulgata* (L.) About 50 mm diam., sometimes even bigger. Varies much in elevation and colour but inside centre *grey* (Fig. 9). The Channel Island species *P. depressa* (Pennant) has the inside centre golden-yellow and the inner margins always rayed. The China limpet (*P. aspera* Lamarck) is porcellanous, inside white or cream with orange centre; more oval than the common limpet and almost always lives in pools. Common.

Blue-rayed limpet *Patina pellucida* (L.) Thin golden-brown, bright blue lines from the beak, 10 mm. Lives on oarweed (*Laminaria* spp.) (Fig. 10). A variety has no blue lines and a thicker flatter shell up to 15 mm. Common on clean rocky shores.

Fig. 9. *Patella vulgata* (L.)

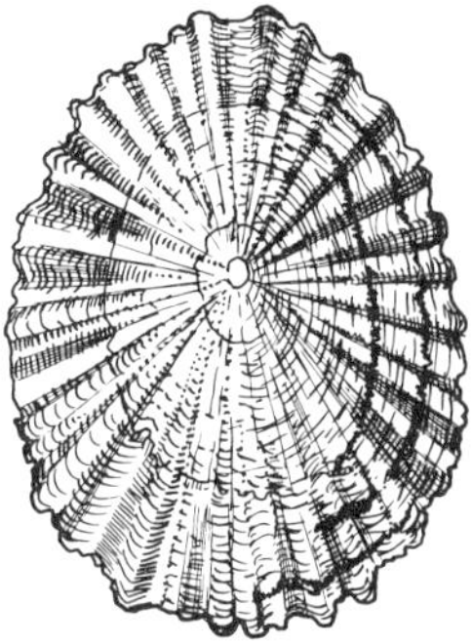

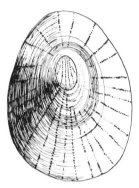

Fig. 10. *Patina pellucida* (L.)

Fig. 11. *Patelloida tessulata* (Müller)

Tortoiseshell limpet *Acmaea testudinalis* (Müller)   Brown and white, size to 15 mm. In the N only, not S of the Isle of Man. Common (Fig. 11). The Pink Tortoiseshell limpet *A. virginea* (Müller) is smaller (10 mm) and pink-rayed; common in pools at LWM.

Top-Shells and Pheasant-Shell

There are sixteen British top-shells and among them are some of our commonest seashells. Many live between tidemarks and all are herbivorous, grazing on seaweeds. There is a thin horny operculum.

Pearly top *Margarites helicinus* (Fabricius)   Thin and smooth, cream or reddish-brown with a blue-green lustre, 4 mm high. Fairly common between tidemarks N of Yorkshire and Dublin (Fig. 12). The scarce *M. groenlandicus* (Gmelin) is similar but larger (8 × 8 mm) with thread-like striae on the upper surface. W Scotland, Orkney, and Shetland.

Fig. 12. *Margarites helicinus* (Fabricius)

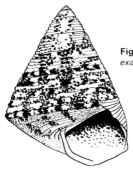

Fig. 13. *Cantharidus exasperatus* (Pennant)

Cantharidus exasperatus (Pennant) A small solid shell, usually pink (sometimes spotted), apex bright pink, 8 mm high. Mainly in the Channel Islands where it is common. (Fig. 13.)

Cantharidus striatus (L.) Yellow-white mottled brown, 10 mm high × 8 mm with 8–9 spiral ridges on each of the last three whorls. Not uncommon, mainly on sea-grass (*Zostera*) about LWM. Montagu's top (*C. montagui* W. Wood) is similar but smaller with only 6–7 ridges on each whorl.

Cleland's top *C. clelandi* (Wood) (Fig. 14). Much larger (15 × 15 mm), a broad shell with a flattened base. The last whorl has 6–7 rows of granules, the lowest forming a conspicuous keel at the base of the body-whorl. Whitish usually spotted red-brown or bright purple. Local but widely distributed.

Pheasant shell (*Tricolia pullus* (L.)) (Fig. 15). Our only British Pheasant-shell is small (only 9 mm high) when compared with its tropical kin but the glossy shell is prettily variegated with red or purple and white. The operculum is like a little white china button. This mollusc is fairly common on seaweeds at LWST but becomes rare in N Scotland.

Painted top *Calliostoma zizyphinum* (L.) A common and pretty species varying much in shape; that illustrated is one of the most usual. Size 27 × 23 mm. A beautiful pure-white variety occurs (notably in Strangford Lough, Northern Ireland). Common on all our rocky coasts from LWM downwards.

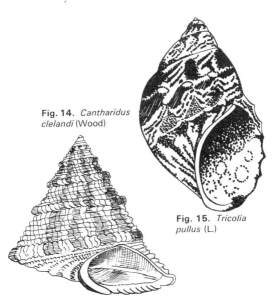

Fig. 14. *Cantharidus clelandi* (Wood)

Fig. 15. *Tricolia pullus* (L.)

(*See* colour plate 2 for all spp. on this page.)

Granulated top *Calliostoma papillosum* (da Costa) Larger (38 × 35 mm) than the Painted top and with a rounded base (that of the latter is flat). The colouring is different, yellow-white variegated red-brown. Rather scarce, from the Channel Islands up the west coast as far N as Oban.

Grey top *Gibbula cineraria* (L.) (Other common names for this common shell are Silver Tommy and Minister.) Usually about 15 × 15 mm but often flatter; the base is bluntly keeled. Common between tide-marks almost everywhere and dredged down to 35 m (70 fm).

Flat top *Gibbula umbilicalis* (da Costa) Flatter than the Grey top and never pyramidal, size 13 mm high × 18 mm across. Striped with red-purple (Grey top is finely lineated with grey-purple). Lives higher up the shore than the Grey top does and is common in the S and W, extending up the west coast as far as Orkney and all round Ireland.

Great top *Gibbula magus* (L.) A large strong shell, size 22 × 30 mm, with a keeled base and wide umbilicus. Sometimes taken at LWEST on shelly sand or fine gravel but more often dredged. Fairly common.

Thick top *Monodonta lineata* (da Costa) A thick clumsy shell, no umbilicus, and with a 'tooth' in the middle of the inner lip. Up to 30 mm high. Lives between tidemarks just below HW of neap tides in the S and W to N Wales but is always very local.

The three little shells depicted on p. 45 have no English names.

Fig. 16.
Tornus subcarinatus
(Montagu)

Fig. 17.
Skenea serpuloides
(Montagu)

Tornus subcarinatus (Montagu)   A distinctive little white shell of 3½–4 whorls, diam. 2–3 mm. Uncommon, living at LWM and below on S and W coasts and in Ireland. (Fig. 16.)

Skenea serpuloides (Montagu)   A tiny white shell (diam. 1 mm) of 3–4 whorls, with the last much the largest. Upperpart of shell quite smooth, underside with many fine spiral lines. Widely distributed from LWM downwards. (Fig. 17.)

Caecum imperforatum (Kanmacher)   A yellow-brown shell with flattened concentric ring-like, close-set. Height 3 mm. The adult shell (illustrated) has no spire (Fig. 18). This species and its ally *C. glabrum* (Montagu) (much smaller and quite smooth) have in youth a loose regular coil of whorls which later falls off, the truncated end being then closed by a shelly plug. *C. imperforatum* is uncommon at LWST on S and W coasts.

Fig. 18. *Caecum imperforatum* (Kanmacher)

45

Chink-Shells and Winkles

Both winkles and chink-shells are common between tidemarks. The chink-shells are distinguished by the well-marked groove on the columella of the shell. Winkles are common on all rocky coasts and often on mud and sand, especially the Periwinkle *Littorina littorea* (L.) which is collected for food in many places.

Banded chink-shell *Lacuna vincta* (Montagu) Shell thin, yellow banded red-brown, not turreted. Up to 10 mm high. Common especially on *Zostera*. The uncommon *Lacuna crassior* (Montagu) has a thick turreted shell with a thick wrinkled periostracum, height 18 mm. (Fig. 19.)

Pale chink-shell *Lacuna pallidula* (da Costa) Thin, green, 10 mm. (Fig. 20.)

Little chink-shell *Lacuna parva* (da Costa) Banded like *L. vincta* but with a very short spire and much smaller (5 mm). (Fig. 21.)

Little winkle *Littorina neritoides* L. (Fig. 22). Grey-brown shell, 6 mm high. Lives in rock crevices at and about HWM. Do not confuse with young Rough Winkles (next species) which often live in the same places; Little Winkles are much more elongated.

Rough winkle *Littorina saxatilis* (Olivi) Most variable in colour, shape and size (up to 16 mm high). One of our commonest species living on all coasts, even on salt-marshes and sometimes in brackish water. The young are produced alive and the species is inedible (*see* colour plate 3).

46

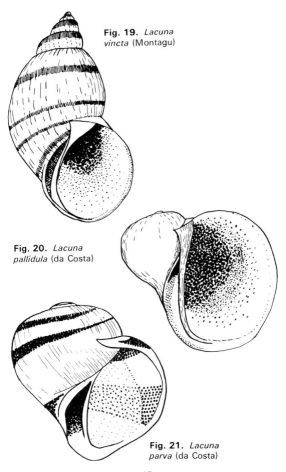

Fig. 19. *Lacuna vincta* (Montagu)

Fig. 20. *Lacuna pallidula* (da Costa)

Fig. 21. *Lacuna parva* (da Costa)

47

Fig. 22. *Littorina neritoides* (L.)

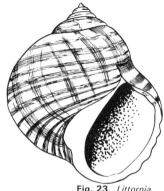

Fig. 23. *Littornia littorea* (L.)

Periwinkle *Littorina littorea* (L.)   Twice the size of the Rough Winkle with a longer and sharper spire. Shells usually black though red and yellow shells are occasionally found. (Fig. 23.)

Flat winkle *Littorina littoralis* (L.) (*see* colour plate 3).   Shell thick, colour very variable. Nearly always associated with the Knotted Wrack (*Ascophyllum*).

Spire-Shells

The Spire-shells (Family Rissoidae) are all very small—about 5 mm long—but some are so common that they must be included. Conchologically the 26 British species can be divided thus: (a) shell spirally striated or smooth, outer lip plain (*Cingula*); (b) shell cancellated or ribbed lengthwise and spirally striated, outer lip usually thickened or with a rib

(*Alvania*); (c) shells mostly ribbed lengthwise, spiral striae inconspicuous, outer lip usually with a rib (*Rissoa*).

Five of the commoner species are:

Cingula semicostata (Montagu)   White, sometimes with faint brown bands. The strong spiral striae distinguish this species. Gregarious on rocky shores. (Fig. 24.)

Cingula cingillus (Montagu)   Yellow-white with brown bands. Also gregarious on rocky shores. Usually live higher up the shore than *C. semicostata* though sometimes the two species occur together. (Fig. 25.)

Alvania crassa (Kanmacher)   White with sharp longitudinal ribs; shell appears slightly twisted. Rocky shores at LWST, feeding on corallines. (Fig. 26.)

Rissoa parva (da Costa)   Our commonest spire-shell and most variable. Sometimes smooth, sometimes ribbed. White variegated brown. Easily

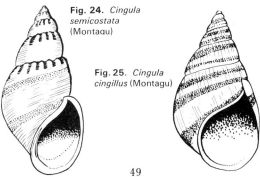

Fig. 24. *Cingula semicostata* (Montagu)

Fig. 25. *Cingula cingillus* (Montagu)

identified by the curved brown streak from the suture to the middle of the outer lip. Very common among small seaweeds between tidemarks. (Fig. 27.)

Rissoa membranacea (J. Adams)   White and brown, aperture with a thick white lip and a toothlike fold on the columella. On *Zostera* and seaweeds at LWST and below. (Fig. 28.)

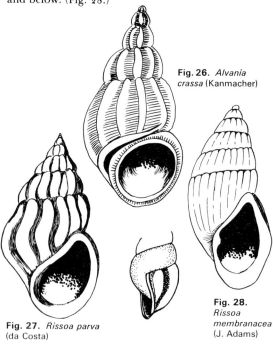

Fig. 26. *Alvania crassa* (Kanmacher)

Fig. 27. *Rissoa parva* (da Costa)

Fig. 28. *Rissoa membranacea* (J. Adams)

Brackish-Water Molluscs

The five species illustrated in Figs 29–33, pp. 51–53 affect more or less brackish water (i.e., water less salt than that of normal seawater). All are relatives of the marine spire-shells and, like them, are small.

Hydrobia ulvae (Pennant)   Occurs in vast numbers on mud-flats and salt-marshes, as well as on muddy-sand shores. Usually about 6 mm high. Many wading birds feed largely on these molluscs. (Fig. 29.)

Fig. 29. *Hydrobia ulvae* (Pennant)

Fig. 30. *Hydrobia ventrosa* (Montagu)

Hydrobia ventrosa (Montagu) (Fig. 30).   Shell smaller than that of *H. ulvae* (usually about 4 mm high), more slender, with a well-marked suture and rounded whorls (in *H. ulvae* the whorls are almost flat). Less common than *H. ulvae* and prefers quiet brackish creeks or lagoons. A closely-allied species (*H. neglecta* Muus) can be told, when alive, by a distinct dark spot near the tip of each tentacle (spot absent in *ventrosa*).

Pseudamnicola confusa (Frauenfeld) A thin shell with 5–6 very convex whorls, the last very large. Height 4–5 mm. Suture deep, umbilicus small and narrow. Lives in brackish and almost fresh water, river-banks and marshes. In E and SE England, S and SE Ireland only. (Fig. 31.)

Mr Jenkins' spire-shell *Potamopyrgus jenkinsi* (Smith) Like a stumpy *Hydrobia ventrosa* but last whorl larger and umbilicus closed, height 4–6 mm. Often has a keel in the middle of each whorl; body and tentacles uniform pale-grey. Not a native of Britain but now widespread here. Country of origin thought to be New Zealand. Lives in fresh or brackish water. (Fig. 32.)

Fig. 31. *Pseudam-nicola confusa* (Frauenfeld)

Fig. 32. *Potamopyrgus jenkinsi* (Smith)

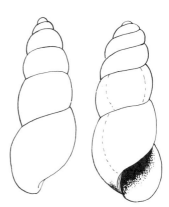

Fig. 33. *Acme subcylindrica* (L.)

Acme subcylindrica (L.) The shell has 6½ whorls when young but only 3½ when adult, older whorls being lost. Suture deep, no umbilicus, height (adult) 5 mm or less. Very local on muddy shores about HWM, Channel Islands and SW England. (Fig. 33.)

Our Smallest Shells!

The Guinness Book of Records should certainly include the first of these! All are tiny and best found by sifting carefully through fine shellsand and by weed-washing (soak small red seaweeds in fresh water overnight when the molluscs will fall to the bottom).

Ammonicera rota (Forbes and Hanley) *The* smallest British shell (diam. 0·5 mm). Flat, with three whorls looking like a miniature ammonite with three spiral keels (occasionally absent). Red-brown or golden.

Not common but widely distributed, rock-pools at LWST. (Fig. 34.)

(Note: there are two other British gastropods, both uncommon, which are almost as small as *Ammonicera*. These are *Tornus imperspicuus* Chaster and *T. unisulcatus* Chaster (relatives of *T. subcarinatus—see* page 45). Both are nearly flat, measuring 0·8 mm across but differ in their sculpture; *T. imperspicuus* has close-set oblique striae across the two whorls, while *T. unisulcatus* has a deep spiral groove encircling the bodywhorl below the periphery).

Omalogyra atomus (Philippi) A tiny flat circular shell (diam. under 1 mm) like a miniature Ramshorn shell (*Planorbis*) of three compact whorls and with a very wide umbilicus; red-brown. Rocky shores, common between tidemarks. (Fig. 35.)

Skeneopsis planorbis (Fabricius) A minute red-brown shell (diam. 1 mm) with four whorls, the last large. Umbilicus very wide and deep. Common between tidemarks. (Fig. 36.)

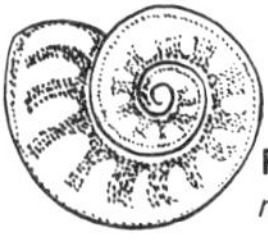

Fig. 34. *Amonicera rota* (Forbes & Hanley)

Fig. 35. *Omalyogyra atomus* (Philippi)

Fig. 36. *Skeneopsis planorbis* (Fabricius)

Augers and Needle-Whelks

Auger or Screw-shell ('Cockspur' in Northern Ireland). *Turritella communis* Risso is well named, and sometimes attains a length of over 50 mm. Empty shells are common on sandy shores but the molluscs live about LWST or deeper, often gregariously, usually where there is an admixture of mud. Widely distributed. (Fig. 37.)

The Needle-whelks comprise two groups of species; in one the aperture of the shell is round and entire (*Bittium*) and in the other group the aperture has a deep notch (*Cerithiopsis, Triphora*).

Small needle-whelk *Bittium reticulatum* (da Costa)   A red-brown shell about 12 mm high. Lives gregariously under stones on rocky shores and on *Zostera* and *Codium* (a green seaweed) at LWST (Fig. 38). The Channel Island *B. simplex* (Jeffreys) is yellow-white, thin and glossy and has no varices; *B. reticulatum* has a varix (a thickened rib) on each whorl.

Cerith needle-whelk *Cerithiopsis tubercularis* (Montagu) (Fig. 39).   Only half the size of *Bittium* and is almost cylindrical, aperture notched. West coast and Ireland, rocky shores at LWST. Usually with the red sponge *Hymeniacidon sanguinea*. There are four more British species of *Cerithiopsis* but all are uncommon.

Reversed needle-whelk *Triphora perversa* (L.)   The only sinistral species. Yellow-brown, height 7 mm. On rocky shores at LWST usually associated with sponges, uncommon. S and W England, Ireland. (Fig. 40.)

Fig. 37. *Turritella communis* (Risso)

Fig. 38. *Bittium reticulatum* (da Costa)

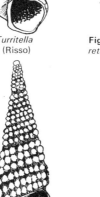

Fig. 39 *Cerithiopsis tubercularis* (Montagu)

Fig. 40 *Triphora perversa* (L.)

Wentletraps

The Wentletraps or staircase-shells comprise five British species but only one is really common. However, they are such attractive shells that all five species are described here though only the first is illustrated. It is thought that wentletraps feed on sea-anemones.

Common wentletrap *Clathrus clathrus* (L.) (*See* colour plate 3). A cream or fawn shell of 15–16 whorls, with sharp longitudinal ridges (9 on body-whorl) which are folded back but not flattened against the spire. Sometimes with 2 or 3 bands of purple-brown. Size 35 × 14 mm. On mud or sandy mud LWST downwards. Widely distributed but rare in the north. (Fig. 41.)

Turton's wentletrap *Clathrus turtonis* (Turton) Larger (45 × 13 mm) with more numerous ribs (12 on body-whorl) which are flattened back against the spire. Pale brown with 2 or 3 purple-brown bands on each whorl. Uncommon; lives below LWST.

Trevelyan's wentletrap *Clathrus trevelyanus* (Johnston) A much thinner shell with 14 ribs on the last two whorls; shell looks turreted. Fawn with white ridges, 17 × 8 mm. Rare but widely distributed.

Clathrus clathratulus (Kanmacher) A slender pyramidal shell, snow-white and thin, of 12–13 whorls with fine sharp ribs (18 on body-whorl). 13 × 4 mm. Rare, rocky shores at LWST, S and W only.

Fig. 41.
*Clathrus
clathrus* (L.)

Fig. 43.
*Eulima
trifasciata*
(J. Adams)

Fig. 42.
Balcis alba
(da Costa)

Cirsotrema commutatum (Monterosato) Like *C. clathrus* (q.v.) but a more conical shell with sharper ridges and a keel encircling the basal whorl. A southern species of which a few shells have been taken in the SW.

The next two species have no English names. They are parasites, living on echinoderms, but empty shells are often met with.

Balcis alba (da Costa) (Fig. 42). An ivory-white glossy shell, 19 × 6 mm. The 'animal' is white and golden-yellow. Locally common.

Eulima trifasciata (J. Adams) A highly-polished yellow-white shell of 10–11 whorls with a pair of tawny spiral bands on each whorl. Size, to 8 × 2 mm. Scarce, but widely distributed. (Fig. 43.)

Violet Snail, Fool's Cap, Chinaman's Hat and Slipper Limpet

Violet Snail *Janthina britannica* (Forbes & Hanley) (*See* colour plate 3.)   A pelagic species from warmer seas than ours but sometimes found washed up on western coasts after a gale. A foam-like raft of air-cells formed by the animal keeps it afloat. Female shells are 20 × 22 mm, males are smaller. Other species of *Janthina* occasionally reach our shores as oceanic waifs.

Fool's Cap *Capulus ungaricus* (L.)   Shells are fairly common but the living mollusc must be dredged for; it lives attached to stones and large shells and attains a diam. of 45 mm. (Fig. 44.)

Chinaman's Hat *Calyptraea chinensis* (L.)   This distinctive shell is locally common, Channel Islands and SW England from LWM downwards. Size, to 19 mm diam. (Fig. 45.)

American Slipper limpet *Crepidula fornicata* (L.)   This North American species was accidentally introduced and is now well established and common along the S and E coasts of England, in Milford Haven and Kenmare in SW Ireland. The shell is pinky-cream or dirty-white, sometimes brown-blotched, about 42 × 28 mm. (Fig. 46.)

In British waters it is a serious pest on commercial oyster-beds as it competes with the oysters for food. It has a curious habit of attaching itself in a 'chain' of up to twelve animals on top of one another. It also changes its sex as it grows; male first, then a transitional form and finally female.

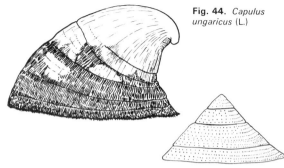

Fig. 44. *Capulus ungaricus* (L.)

Fig. 45. *Calyptraea chinensis* (L.)

Fig. 46. *Crepidula fornicata* (L.)

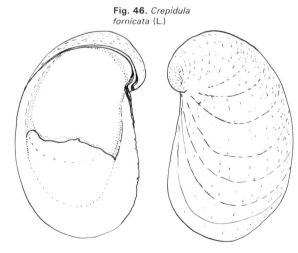

60

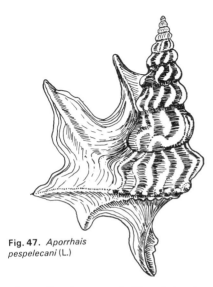

Fig. 47. *Aporrhais pespelecani* (L.)

The Pelican's-Foot Shell and the Cormorant's-Foot Shell

Pelican's-Foot shell *Aporrhais pespelecani* (L.) (Fig. 47.) This species is unmistakeable when adult but the young shells are spindle-shaped with a long straight canal; the enlarged and fingered outer lip is developed with maturity. Up to 54 mm long. Common except in the Channel Islands and Scilly. The rare Cormorant's-Foot shell *Aporrhais serresianus* (Michaud) is like a small thin Pelican's-Foot shell but with only 7–8 whorls (former species has 12 whorls) and the 'fingers' are far longer and finer, one usually extending beyond the tip of the spire. In deep water off Shetland, Arran and SW Ireland.

The next curious-looking mollusc is a parasite upon sea-urchins where it creeps about among the spines, apparently feeding upon the epidermis.

Pelseneeria stylifera (Turton)   Amber or whitish in colour, smooth and glossy, 5 × 3 mm. Apparently now rare, though widely distributed. (Fig. 48.)

Fig. 48. *Pelseneeria stylifera* (Turton)

Fig. 49. *Trichotropis borealis* (Broderip & Sowerby)

Trichotropis borealis (Broderip & Sowerby)   A whitish turreted shell, rather spindle-shaped of seven sharply-keeled whorls with cord-like spiral ribs. The pale brown periostracum forms bristly points on the chief ribs. Size 10 × 6 mm. Local but not rare; North Sea to Shetland, W Scotland and NE Ireland. (Fig. 49.)

Necklace Shells

So-called from the fancied resemblance of their spawn-coil to a torque or necklace. In the USA they are called Moon-shells. The first two species, which are also the commonest, live in large sandy bays burrowing just below the surface. Necklace shells hunt bivalves on which they prey, boring a neat bevelled hole into the victim's shell and then rasping out the fleshy contents. When feeding the Necklace shell may take its own weight in bivalve flesh.

If attacked by a starfish in turn the common Necklace shell can cover much of its shell with an extension of the soft slippery body. The starfish can get no grip on this and retires defeated.

Common Necklace shell *Natica catena* (da Costa) Fawn-colour with one row of brown markings on each whorl, 34 mm high. Its spawn-coil is usually about 20–30 mm wide; it is formed of egg-cases embedded in a jelly stiffened with sand-grains. (Fig. 50.)

Alder's Necklace shell *Natica alderi* (Forbes) (Fig. 51). Less than half the size of *N. catena* and more oval, with five rows of red-brown markings on the body-whorl. The spawn-coil is smooth and flexible. Montagu's necklace shell *Natica montagui* (Forbes) has a thick fawn-coloured shell (aperture red-brown) of 5–6 swollen whorls, 12 × 10 mm. Not uncommon beyond tidemarks, more frequent in the N. There are three more British species but all are scarce. The rare Iceland Necklace shell *Amauropis islandica* (Gmelin) is an allied species; a thin white shell, an elongated oval in shape of

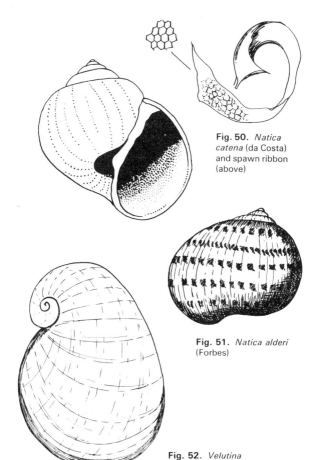

Fig. 50. *Natica catena* (da Costa) and spawn ribbon (above)

Fig. 51. *Natica alderi* (Forbes)

Fig. 52. *Velutina velutina* (Müller)

5–7 rounded whorls. Suture conspicuously channelled, a small narrow umbilicus. Size 18 × 13 mm. In the N and E only.

Velvet shell *Velutina velutina* (Müller) Whitish-brown, often tinged pink, beneath the thick brown periostracum which gives the shell its popular name. Size 18 × 14 mm. Generally distributed but more common in the north. (Fig. 52.)

Cowries, Poached-Egg Shell and Volute

Of Cowries, that tropical group so beloved of shell-collectors, we have only two species in Britain (*see* colour plate 5). These are:

Trivia monacha (da Costa) and *T. arctica* (Montagu), both known as Cowrie, Groat, Grottie-Buckie, Nun and so on. In life the Cowrie looks like a small orange slug for the shell is almost hidden by the mantle of the mollusc. The Spotted Cowrie (*T. monacha*) has three purple-brown spots on the back of the shell.

The European Cowrie (*T. arctica*) (Fig. 53) is usually smaller and has no spots. Size in both species up to 10 mm long.

Both species are generally distributed, living at LWM and below.

Volute *Erato voluta* (Montagu) A smooth white shell with 15 small 'teeth' within the outer lip and 2 or 3 slight folds at the base of the shell. Size 12 × 7 mm. The larval stage of this mollusc has a thin snail-shaped shell which is later lost. Like *Trivia* spp. the Volute feeds on compound ascidians. Scarce but

Fig. 54. *Erato voluta* (Montagu)

Fig. 53. *Trivia arctica* (Montagu)

Fig. 55. *Lamellaria perspicua* (L.)

widely distributed on gravel or sand 0·5–45 m (1–90 fm), becoming rare in the N. (Fig. 54.)

Poached-egg shell *Simnia patula* (Pennant) Yellow-white with very fine spiral lines, size 22 × 12 mm. Feeds on Dead Men's Fingers (*Alcyonium*). A scarce species living well below LWM and mainly in the SW through occasionally it is found as far north as Orkney (*see* colour plate 5).

Lamellaria perspicua (L.) (Fig. 55) has no English name. It is a flattened slug-like animal about 20 mm long, varying much in colour but often greyish. Feeds on ascidians. The white shell is internal, about 12 × 8 mm. Widely distributed from LWM downwards. Another species (*L. latens* (Müller)) is much smaller and the shell is flatter with a proportionately larger aperture.

Three Rarities!

The three species illustrated by Figs 56, 57 and 58 may conveniently be grouped together as all barely reach British waters and are very rare. All are such large distinctive shells that there should be no difficulty in identifying them should any reader be fortunate enough to encounter a specimen!

Galeodea rugosa (L.)   This fine species, a relative of the massive Helmet-shells of the tropics, has been dredged alive off SW Ireland and also S of the Scillies. Shells have been taken in the last few years in deepish water in the Dingle area, Co. Kerry. The shell is whitish or flesh-colour, size about 90 × 57 mm. (Fig. 56.)

Ranella olearium (L.)   A mediterranean species that just manages to get included in the British list on the strength of several living specimens dredged in 50–100 fm off the S of Ireland. The shell is flesh-pink or yellowish beneath the brown periostracum; a British (or rather, Irish) specimen measured 122 × 63 mm. (Fig. 57.)

Fig. 56. *Galeodea rugosa* (L.)

Fig. 57. *Ranella olearium* (L.)

Fig. 58. *Charonia lampas* (L.)

Charonia lampas (L.) The Triton. Also a mediterranean species, of which a few specimens were obtained in Guernsey during the last century. No more were taken until 1972 when no fewer than three living examples were dredged from the waters around Guernsey. The shell is usually encrusted with marine growths but when clear it is whitish variegated with coffee-brown. One of the Guernsey specimens measured 220 mm long. (Fig. 58.)

Dog-Whelks and Sting-Winkles (Tingles or Drills)

All these molluscs are carnivorous and some are serious pests on oyster-beds.

Trophonopsis truncatus (Ström) (Fig. 59). Yellow-white or flesh-pink, with 16–20 ribs. 15 mm high. Fairly common. The allied *Trophonopsis muricatus* (Montagu) is turreted and the numerous ribs are crossed by spiral striae giving a prickly look. Rather scarce, mostly S and W.

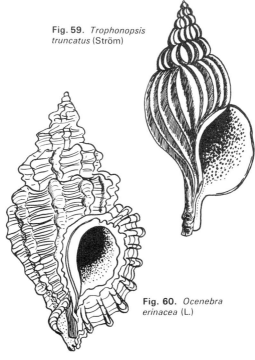

Fig. 59. *Trophonopsis truncatus* (Ström)

Fig. 60. *Ocenebra erinacea* (L.)

Sting-winkle *Ocenebra erinacea* (L.) (Fig. 60). Yellow-white; the canal is open in young specimens, closed in adults. Size 42 × 20 mm. Preys on barnacles, oysters and carpet-shells. Common in the S, rarer in the N. *Ocenebra aciculata* (Lamarck) is much smaller (12 mm), red-brown and lives in the Channel Islands only.

American Tingle or Oyster-Drill *Urosalpinx cinerea* (Say) This is like a small *Ocenebra erinacea* but canal is always open. Whitish often with brown spiral lines, size 30 × 17 mm. Preys on oysters and is a pest on oyster-beds. (Fig. 61.)

Netted Dog-Whelk *Nassarius reticulatus* (L.) Fawn or whitish, often with a purple-brown band on each whorl. 26 mm. Common on shelly gravel about LWM. Feeds on carrion, as do the other species of *Nassarius*. (Fig. 62.)

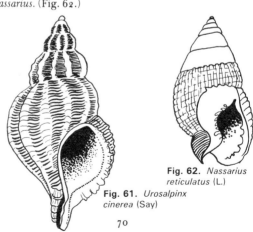

Fig. 62. *Nassarius reticulatus* (L.)

Fig. 61. *Urosalpinx cinerea* (Say)

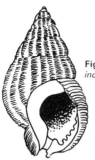

Fig. 63. *Nassarius incrassatus* (Ström)

Thick-lipped Dog-Whelk *Nassarius incrassatus* (Ström) (Fig. 63). White, pink or purple, always with a brown basal blotch. Up to 14 × 7 mm. Common on rocky shores about LWM. The uncommon *Nassarius pygmaeus* (Lamarck) is like *incrassatus* but is more slender, has no basal blotch and has a varix on each whorl. Size 12 × 4 mm.

Common Dog-Whelk *Nucella lapillus* (L.) (*see* colour plate 4). White yellow or purple, sometimes banded. Banded shells appear to be much more frequent in the south and west, and are distinctly rare in the north. White-shelled animals have fed on barnacles, purple shells indicate a diet of mussels. Yellow is thought to be linked in some way with the degree of exposure on the shore where the animals live.

Usually about 35 mm long but occasional giants are found up to 60 mm. The Bristol Channel supplies most of these giants from lobster pots, and they are not found between tidemarks. One of the commonest intertidal molluscs; preys upon barnacles and bivalves, boring round holes with straight

71

sides in the victim's shell and then extracting the living tissues.

The yellow eggs are like groups of grains of wheat set on end.

Whelks, Buckies and Spindle-Shells

These molluscs are all carnivorous, eating fresh dead crabs or fish, and are often taken in lobster-pots having been lured there by the bait. The Whelk *Buccinum undatum* is largely eaten but not the other species.

Common Spindle *Colus gracilis* (da Costa) (Fig. 64.) White, with a canal turned sharply to the left (when shell is held with aperture facing you), and a twisted mammiform apex. Size about 76 × 32 mm. Common, but becoming rare in the south. The rare Iceland Spindle *Colus islandicus* (Gmelin) is twice the size with a long straight canal. Another spindle is *C. howsei* (Marshall) like a small *C. gracilis* but apex is regularly blunt; height 45 mm. Mainly found in the N. *C. jeffreysianus* (Fischer) is rather like the last species but much larger (58 mm) more swollen, a short wide canal and the surface is slightly decussated. Scarce, Bristol Channel southward.

Buckie or Red Whelk *Neptunea antiqua* (L.) (Fig. 65). Yellow-white or flesh-colour, aperture sometimes orange. From 100–200 mm. Common except in S. England and Channel Islands.

Whelk *Buccinum undatum* (L.) (Fig. 66.) (sometimes also called Buckie) Edible and common, varying

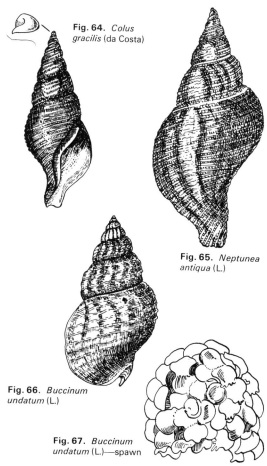

Fig. 64. *Colus gracilis* (da Costa)

Fig. 65. *Neptunea antiqua* (L.)

Fig. 66. *Buccinum undatum* (L.)

Fig. 67. *Buccinum undatum* (L.)—spawn

much in size and shape, from 10–165 mm high, but usually about 60 mm. Intertidal specimens rather small with thick shells and a purple-brown aperture. Eggs resemble a ball of froth, each capsule containing several eggs, only a few of which hatch and eat the other eggs. The rare Humphreys' Whelk *Buccinum humphreysianum* (Bennett) (45 mm) is yellow-white variegated red-brown with a tiny triangular operculum (in *B. undatum* the operculum is oval). Deep water off Shetland, Hebrides, S and W of Ireland.

Rare North Sea Buckies

These three large species are all collectors' pieces and are not likely to come the way of a beach-collector, but specimens might be got from fishermen. None have common names.

Beringius turtoni (Bean) The shell is white beneath the yellow-green periostracum and has 7–8 whorls with numerous spiral ridges and a conical apex. Up to 140 × 65 mm. In deep water off NE coast and Shetland. (Fig. 68.)

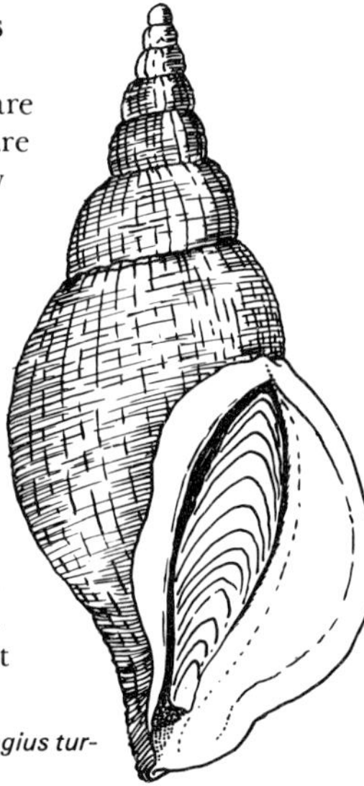

Fig. 68. *Beringius turtoni* (Bean)

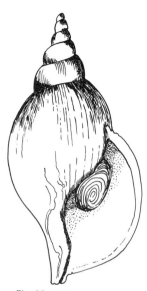

Fig. 69. *Volu-
topsius norwegicus*
(Gmelin)

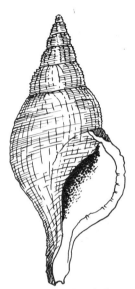

Fig. 70. *Troschelia
berniciensis* (King)

Volutopsius norwegicus (Gmelin) A thin creamy
white shell with 5–6 swollen whorls and a bulbous
apex to the short spire. Size 105 × 50 mm. Lives with
Beringius and in the same localities. (Fig. 69.)

Troschelia berniciensis (King) This is, properly
speaking, not a Buckie at all but a member of the
family Fasciolariidae which includes the Tulip shells
of the Caribbean. The shell is pinkish-white under
the brown-yellow periostracum, and the eight

whorls have numerous fine spiral ridges. Size 125 × 55 mm. (Fig. 70.)

Shells *might* be found along the coast between Banff and the Humber and any unusual large 'Buckie' from the North Sea should be retained for investigation.

Turrids, or Turret-Shells

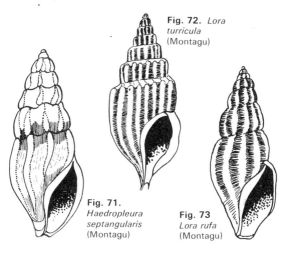

Fig. 72. *Lora turricula* (Montagu)

Fig. 71. *Haedropleura septangularis* (Montagu)

Fig. 73 *Lora rufa* (Montagu)

The shells of Turrids are spindle-shaped with a long spire, pointed base and the outer lip notched. The canal is nearly straight and the columella smooth. In

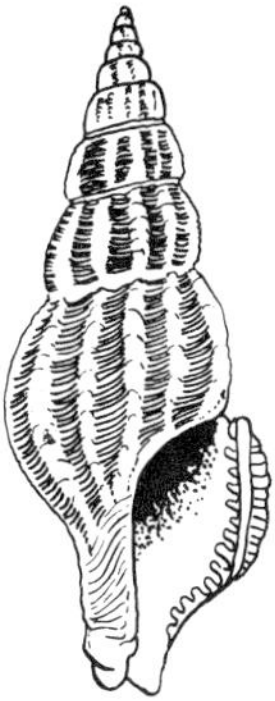

Fig. 75. *Philbertia linearis* (Montagu)

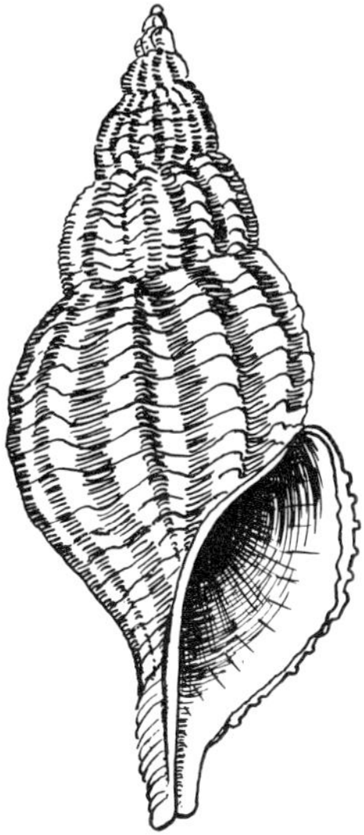

Fig. 74. *Mangelia nebula* (Montagu)

Fig. 76. *Philbertia gracilis* (Montagu)

the genus *Philbertia* (6 species) the outer lip is grooved within (it is smooth in the other genera).

There are about eighteen British Turrids, all of them carnivorous. Shells are not uncommon but living animals are seldom obtained.

Haedropleura septangularis (Montagu)   A very thick red-brown shell with seven strong ribs which do not reach the base. Height 15 mm. Rather uncommon, SW and W coasts, Ireland. (Fig. 71.)

Lora turricula (Montagu)   Turreted, white or pink, height 15 mm. A northern species, not uncommon except in the S and SW. (Fig. 72.)

Lora rufa (Montagu) Fawn-colour, orange or purple-brown, 9 mm high. Also fairly common (shells). Lives LWST downwards off all coasts. (Fig. 73.)

Mangelia nebula (Montagu) Chocolate-colour, the 10 or 12 ribs often paler, and the whole shell impressed with very fine spiral striae. Size 11 × 3·5 mm. Shells fairly common. Lives from LWST down to 25 m (50 fm) and is generally distributed. (Fig. 74.)

Philbertia gracilis (Montagu) (Fig. 76). The largest Turrid, shells up to 25 mm. Fawn or red-brown, a white band on the periphery. There are 14–16 ribs on the body-whorl, crossed by spiral striae. Scarce, but generally distributed.

Philbertia linearis (Montagu) One of the more common species. Yellow-white with red-brown lines, apex orange or purple. Height 9 mm. Lives between tidemarks (Fig. 75). *Philbertia leufroyi* (Michaud) is rather like *P. linearis* but has 14–18 ribs on the body-whorl (*P. linearis* has only 12). Lives in the same habitats but is less common.

Bubble-Shells

Bubble-shells include such diverse animals as the Beer Barrel shell (*Acteon*) in which the animal can withdraw completely into the shell, to the Lobe-shell (*Philine aperta*) where the shell is entirely internal. Most of the species live on sand or mud, some burrowing shallowly, and some crawling on the surface.

Beer Barrel *Acteon tornatilis* (L.) About 33 mm high. Common on sandy shores where it burrows at LWST. It preys on the minute shelled animals known as Foraminifera. (*See* colour plate 5.)

Cylinder shell *Cylichna cylindracea* (Pennant) A white shell, the base often rust-stained, 12 mm. Common on muddy sand almost everywhere. (Fig. 77.)

Canoe shell *Tricla lignaria* (L.) A yellow-white shell under the chestnut periostracum and up to 50 mm long. Common in sandy bays around our coasts though seldom taken living as it normally lives beyond LWM. It lives on other molluscs especially bivalve fry. (*See* colour plate 5.)

Retusa retusa (Maton & Rackett) A white shell with longitudinal striae at the top fading out at the base. Size 5 mm. Common on muddy ground about LWM and downwards. (Fig. 78.)

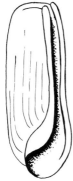

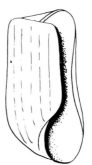

Fig. 77 *Cylichna cylindracea* (Pennant)

Fig. 78 *Retusa retusa* (Maton & Rackett)

Retusa alba (Kanmacher) (Fig. 79). Much broader than *R. retuse* and lacks the striae, spire varying much in length. Usually about 5 × 3 mm. Common in muddy estuaries throughout Britain and often in brackish water; gregarious at LWM. Preys on the little snail *Hydrobia ulvae* which is abundant in the same habitats as *R. alba*. There are two other species of *Retusa,* both very small and not common.

The species illustrated below all have the shell partly concealed by the soft body of the animal or else the shell is entirely internal (*Philine, Pleurobranchus, Berthella, Berthellina*).

Thin Bubble-shell *Akera bullata* (Müller) (Fig. 80). A thin white shell, 30 × 21 mm, partly hidden by the large 'animal'; flits about actively by means of its large lobes. Grazes on green algae and lives on tidal mudflats, fairly common and gregarious. A somewhat similar Bubble-shell is *Haminoea navicula* (da Costa) with a fragile greenish-yellow shell (25 × 20 mm) which also lives on mud-flats, but only in the S and W. It preys on bivalves, swallowing them whole.

Fig. 79. *Retusa alba* (Kannmacher)

Fig. 80. *Akera bullata* (Müller)

Plate 1 Ear-shell or Ormer *(Haliotis tuberculata)*;
a, from above; b, showing interior

Plate 2 Great Top *(Gibbula magus)* 2. Grey Top *(Gibbula cineraria)* 3. Flat Top *(Gibbula umbilicalis)* 4. Granulated Top *(Calliostoma papillosum)* 5. Thick Top *(Monodonta lineata)* 6. Painted Top *(Calliostoma zizyphinum)*

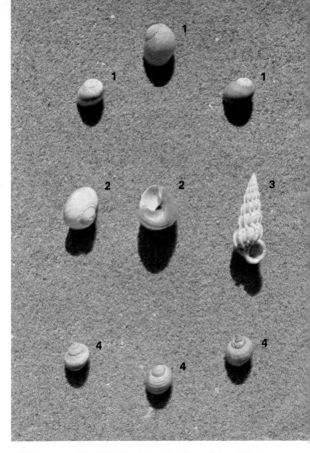

Plate 3 1. Flat Winkle *(Littorina littoralis)* 2. Violet Snail *(Janthina britannica)* 3. Wentletrap *(Clathrus clathrus)* 4. Rough Winkle *(Littorina saxatilis)*

Plate 4 Dog Whelks *(Nucella lapillus)*, showing variation

Plate 5 Lobe-shell *(Philine quodripartita)* 2. European Cowry *(Trivia arctica)* 3. Spotted Cowry *(Trivia monacha)* 4. Canoe Shell *(Tricla lignaria)* 5. Poached-Egg-Shell *(Simnia patula)* 6. Beer-Barrel *(Aceteon tornatilis)*

Plate 6 1. Variegated Scallop *(Chlamys varia)*
2. Tiger Scallop *(Chlamys tigerina)* 3. Seven-rayed
Scallop *(Chlamys septemradiata)*

Plate 7 I. Rough Tellin *(Tellina squalida)* 2. Sunset Shell *(Gari fervensis)* 3. Thin Tellin *(Tellina tenuis)* 4. Baltic Tellin *(Macoma balthica)*

Plate 8 1. Banded Carpet-Shell *(Venerupis rhomboides)*
2. Golden Carpet-Shell *(Venerupis aurea)* 3. Pullet
Carpet-Shell *(Venerupis pullastra)*

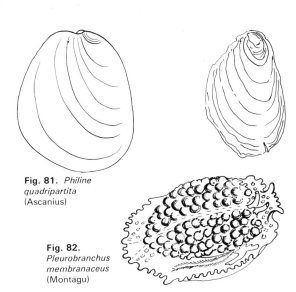

Fig. 81. *Philine quadripartita* (Ascanius)

Fig. 82. *Pleurobranchus membranaceus* (Montagu)

Lobe-shell *Philine quadripartita* (Ascanius) (Fig. 81). The white shell (20 × 15 mm) is quite smooth and internal; the living mollusc, also white, looks like a rather odd sea-slug divided into four lobes. Eats marine worms and small bivalves. Common, burrowing in sand at LWST. There are seven other members of the family Philinidae but all are very small (largest 6 × 5 mm), six are delicately sculptured and one is smooth with a conspicuous spire.

Pleurobranchus membranaceus (Montagu) (Fig. 82). The large animal (up to 100 mm long) is reddish-brown, tortoise-shaped, tuberculated, with an internal shell which is ear-shaped, and membranous, pale red-brown fading to silvery, size 50 × 30 mm. Mainly in S and W. Two allied species (*Berthella plumula* (Montagu) and *Berthellina engeli* (Gardiner) have pale-yellow bodies, are only 25 mm long, and the shells are white.

Pyramid-Shells

The Pyramid-shells (about 43 British species!) are all small, the largest only 9 mm high and nearly all have white shells. They are parasites, living by sucking the juices of other animals (molluscs, worms, echinoderms). Usually only the empty shell is found

Fig. 84. *Turbonilla elegantissima* (Montagu)

Fig. 83. *Chrysallida spiralis* (Montagu)

Fig. 85. *Menestho divisa* (J. Adams)

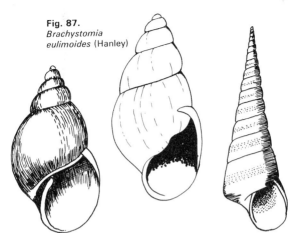

Fig. 87.
*Brachystomia
eulimoides* (Hanley)

Fig. 86.
*Brachystomia
scalaris* (Macgillivray)

Fig. 88. *Eulimella
macandrei* (Forbes)

because in many cases the host-animal is not yet
known. None of them have common names.

Chrysallida spiralis (Montagu) (Fig. 83).   One of the
commonest, easily known by the 6–8 spiral striae which
encircle the base of the shell and cut off the strong
longitudinal ribs. This species is associated with the
tube-building worm *Sabellaria*. Another common
species is *Chrysallida obtusa* (Brown) which has 5 or 6
whorls with about 30 strong ribs; the ribs are crossed
below the periphery by two spiral striae. There is a
'tooth' on the columella and the species lives on
oysters.

Turbonilla elegantissima (Montagu) (Fig. 84).   Twelve
whorls with 20–25 ribs, the largest British Pyramid-

shell, up to 9 mm high. Fairly common, associated with several kinds of marine worms. Four other species of *Turbonilla* have coloured shells—fawn or yellow banded red-brown—but none is common.

Menestho divisa (J. Adams)   Only 3 mm high. Uncommon, but widely distributed. (Fig. 85.)

Brachystomia scalaris (Macgillivray)   Also 3 mm. Common, living among mats of mussels (*Mytilus*). Has a small umbilicus and 'tooth' on the columella. (Fig. 86.)

Brachystomia eulimoides (Hanley) (Fig. 87.) is another common species, 5 mm. The shell has a long bodywhorl and no umbilicus. Lives on the 'ears' of the scallops *Pecten maximus* and *Chlamys opercularis*.

Eulimella macandrei (Forbes)   Has 11 or 12 polished flattened whorls angulated at the base, 8·5 mm. Rare. (Fig. 88.)

Pulmonate Gastropods and Tusk-Shells

The large sub-class Pulmonata (air-breathing) includes nearly the land and freshwater molluscs, and is very sparingly represented among the marine species. Only four species can be termed marine and even these live at or above HWM.

Phytia myosotis (Draparnaud) (Fig. 89).   A fat little grey-brown shell, 6–8 mm with 3 tooth-like folds on the columella and usually 2–3 within the outer lip as well. Sometimes abundant on salt-marshes, often living under Sea Aster (*Aster tripolium*). There is a white, more strictly marine variety (var. *denticulata* (Mon-

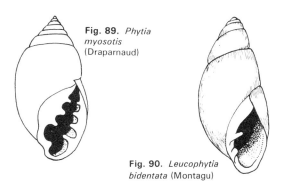

Fig. 89. *Phytia myosotis* (Draparnaud)

Fig. 90. *Leucophytia bidentata* (Montagu)

tagu)) which lives on brown seaweeds high up on very sheltered shores.

Leucophytia bidentata (Montagu)   A cream shell like a little roll of candle wax, lives among *Fucus* or under stones at HWM on sheltered shores; often associated with *Cingula cingillus*. Do not confuse with the marine form of *Phytia* which is larger, fatter and has 3 'teeth'—*Leucophytia* has only two. Widely distributed but local. (Fig. 90.)

Otina ovata (Brown)   A tiny (2 mm) ear-shaped shell, red-brown. Alive, it looks like a little blob of jelly, the animal being rather large for the shell. In empty barnacle shells close to HWM. Perhaps not rare but hard to find. (Fig. 91.)

The small group of Tusk-shells live in sand at LWST and in deeper water. They live buried with only a small part of the posterior (narrow) end sticking up into the water. There are five British species but only two are likely to be encountered.

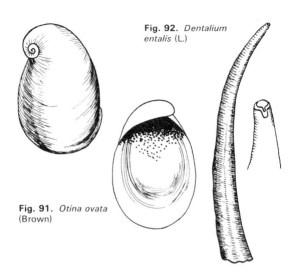

Fig. 92. *Dentalium entalis* (L.)

Fig. 91. *Otina ovata* (Brown)

Common Tusk-shell *Dentalium entalis* (L.) (Fig. 92). Ivory-white shell with a notch in posterior end. Size 35 mm. Frequent in N, less so in S. *Dentalium vulgare* (da Costa) has fine longitudinal striae at posterior end of shell and no notch. S and W England, Ireland. The wampum currency of Red Indians was made of an American tusk-shell.

Squid, Cuttle-Fish and Octopus

These animals form the class Cephalopoda and are the most highly organized of the Mollusca. All are active carnivores, seizing their prey with sucker-armed tentacles and having jaws like a parrot's beak. Their ability to change colour and to emit an inky cloud is well known and some can move rapidly by means of a kind of jet propulsion. Squids and cuttles have five pairs of tentacles, one pair longer than the rest, but octopods have only four pairs, of equal length and retractable.

Common Cuttle *Sepia officinalis* (L.) (Fig. 93). Up to 48 cm long. The familiar 'cuttle-bone' is the internal shell of this species. Widely distributed but most frequent in the S. A much smaller species (*Sepia elegans* (Orbigny)) is about 125 mm long with a much smaller slenderer 'bone' often tinged pink.

Common Squid *Loligo forbesi* (Steenstrup)   Length 20–75 cm. The internal shell of this species is a horny 'pen' sometimes found washed up on the shore. (Fig. 94.)

Fig. 94. *Loligo forberi* (Steenstrup) with 'pen'

Fig. 93. *Sepia officianalis* (L.), with 'bone'

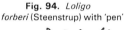

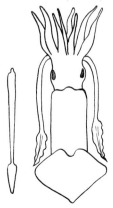

Common Octopus *Octopus vulgaris* (Lamarck)
Has a bag-shaped body, no internal shell and two
rows of suckers on each tentacle. Despite its name
not common, occurring only in the S.

Curled Octopus *Eledone cirrhosa* (Lamarck)   Up to
50 cm. Easily distinguished by its having only one
row of suckers on each tentacle. Frequent, much
commoner in the N.

Spirula peronii (Lamarck)   The pearly internal
shell of this tropical cephalopod is occasionally cast
upon our shores. (Fig. 95.)

Fig. 95. *Spirula
peronii* (Lamarck)

Nut-Shells

These bivalves (for method of measuring bivalves see
p. 13) all have a characteristic comb-like arrange-
ment of 'teeth' on the hinge-line. They are the most
primitive of bivalves.

Common Nut-shell *Nucula nucleus* (L.) (Fig. 96).   As
its name infers, this is the commonest of the Nut-shells.
The valves are pearly inside, margins crenulated all
round, 12 mm across. The next most frequent species
is *Nucula Turgiaa* (Leckenby & Marshall) with a very
glossy and more acutely triangular shell than *N.
nucleus*. *N. nucleus* has 15 'teeth' in front of the beak and

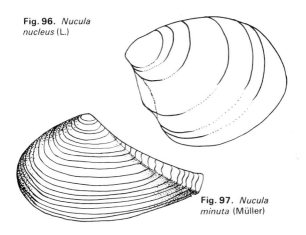

Fig. 96. *Nucula nucleus* (L.)

Fig. 97. *Nucula minuta* (Müller)

25 behind, *N. turgida* has 12 in front and 20 behind. The two species often live together but *N. nucleus* is usually the commoner. The largest nut-shell is *N. sulcata* (Bronn) (18 mm across) which has the inner margins crenulated in front only. Finally, the rather scarce Thin Nut-shell (*N. tenuis* (Montagu)) is easily distinguished because the margins of the valves are quite smooth.

Nucula minuta (Müller) A distinctive shell with 30 fine transverse ribs and two ridges from beak to truncated posterior. 15 mm long. Generally distributed. (Fig. 97.)

Saddle-Oysters or Jingle-Shells

The four British species of Saddle-oysters all adhere closely to rocks or old shells by means of a calcified

89

cable of coalesced byssal threads passing through a pear-shaped opening in the lower valve. The shells are often thin and beautifully coloured, especially in the first-mentioned species; the shell frequently takes the shape of the object to which it is attached, being ribbed if the substratum is a scallop, for instance.

Saddle-Oyster *Anomia ephippium* (L.)   Much the largest species, up to 60 mm across (exceptionally up to 100 mm). White, yellow, pink or brown, silvery within. Apart from size it can easily be distinguished by having *three* muscular impressions in the upper (entire) valve. Common from LWM downwards. (Fig. 98.)

Monia patelliformis (L.)   Half the size, shell often streaked or rayed with red-brown, interior of upper valve white. Has only *two* muscle-scars which show fine radial markings. (Fig. 99.)

Fig. 98. *Anomia ephippium* (L.)

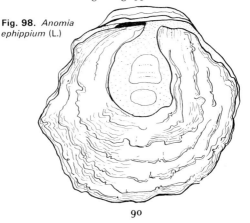

Fig. 99.
*Monia
patelliformis*
(L.)–muscle
scars

Fig. 100.
Monia squama
(Gmelin)—
muscle scars

Fig. 101.
*Heteranomia
squamula* (L.)—
muscle scars

Monia squama (Gmelin) (Fig. 100). Like *Monia patelliformis* but interior of upper valve usually dark green. The two muscle-scars are radially striated but are joined together to form one confluent scar (in *patelliformis* they are quite separate). Apparently the least common of the saddle-oysters.

Heteranomia squamula (L.) The smallest species, only about 12 mm. Shell white with two muscle-scars which are not radially striated. (Fig. 101.) Common in *Laminaria* holdfasts, on stones and old shells, even on living lobsters.

Dog-Cockle and Ark-Shells

In these shells the tubercular 'teeth' are arranged in a continuous line instead of in two separate rows in the same line as in *Nucula*.

Dog-Cockle or Comb-shell *Glycymeris glycymeris* (L.) A large thick shell up to 70 mm diam., oblique or nearly circular, yellow-white variegated red-

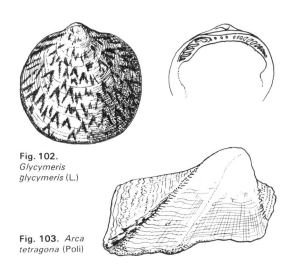

Fig. 102.
*Glycymeris
glycymeris* (L.)

Fig. 103. *Arca
tetragona* (Poli)

brown. Burrows shallowly, living in depths 14–45 m
(7–90 fm). Common. (Fig. 102.)

Noah's Ark or Ark-shell *Arca tetragona* (Poli) An
odd deformed-looking shell rather like a box, up to
45 mm long. The shell is often distorted by being
wedged into a rock-crevice, attached firmly by its
byssus. Colour, yellowish-white mottled red-brown.
Lives on all our rocky coasts from LWM downwards.
(Fig. 103.)

Milky Ark *Arca lactea* (L.) White beneath the
brown hairy periostracum, sometimes rhomboidal
in shape, sometimes triangular. Not uncommon in
the S, especially in the Channel Islands. (Fig. 104.)

Fig. 104. *Arca lactea* (L.)

Mussels

Common mussel *Mytilus edulis* (L.) Abundant almost everywhere and much esteemed as food. Varies a great deal in size, from 18–130 mm, those nearest HWM are the smallest. Often occurs in vast beds, the most profitable beds being those just about LWM where food is plentiful, ensuring large plump mussels. Often contains small pearls. (Fig. 105.)

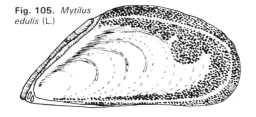

Fig. 105. *Mytilus edulis* (L.)

Horse mussel *Modiolus modiolus* (L.) (Fig. 106). Our largest mussel, often 123–150 mm. Distinguished from common mussels by the beaks being a little way from the tip of the shell (in the common mussel the beaks are at the very tip of the shell). The periostracum is yellow-brown and often fringed, especially in young specimens; the fringe-filaments have plain edges. The Horse mussel is much used for bait, and eaten by mankind in Glasgow. Lives in rock-pools LWST, in the holdfasts of the big oarweeds (*Laminaria*), and plentifully in deeper water.

A record-breaking giant specimen measured almost 230 mm.

Tulip mussel *Modiolus adriaticus* (Lamarck)   Shell 38 mm, thin and glossy, yellowish with red or purple rays, and a very thin periostracum like varnish. Rather uncommon, but widely distributed except in Scotland where it is very rare. (Fig. 107.)

Modiolus barbatus (L.)   Is only 30 mm and has a yellow or scarlet shell under the fringed

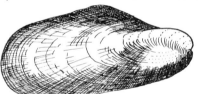

Fig. 106. *Modiolus modiolus* (L.)

Fig. 107. *Modiolus adriaticus* (Lamarck)

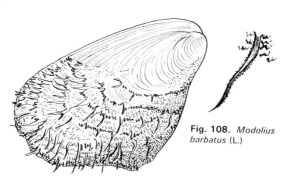

Fig. 108. *Modolius barbatus* (L.)

Fig. 109. *Musculus marmoratus* (Forbes)

periostracum, which has barbed filaments. Not uncommon, S and W coasts and Ireland. (Fig. 108.)

Musculus marmoratus (Forbes) (Fig. 109). A thin rhomboidal shell, yellow mottled red-brown beneath the pale-green periostracum. There are 15–18 ribs on the anterior and 20–25 on the posterior of each valve, with the centre smooth. 17 mm long. Common, often found embedded in sea-squirts (simple ascidians). Another common species is *Musculus discors* (L.) which

95

has only 10–12 ribs on the anterior and 30–40 on the posterior, and a yellow-brown shell. About 11 mm long. The uncommon Corduroy mussel *Musculus niger* (Gray) is up to 50 mm long and purple-black, with 12 ribs on the anterior and 50–60 fine close-set ribs on the posterior. NE England and Scotland only.

Oysters

Native Oyster *Ostrea edulis* (L.)   The familiar and succulent native has a shell more or less rounded in outline with a white muscle scar. Adult shells are about 100 mm across. On all our coasts from Cornwall to Shetland but now extinct or nearly so in many places. During the last century over-fishing

Fig. 110. *Ostrea edulis* (L.)

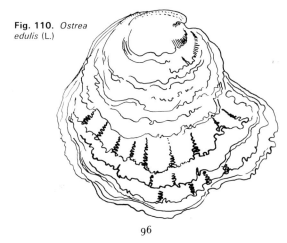

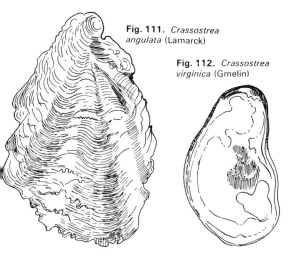

Fig. 111. *Crassostrea angulata* (Lamarck)

Fig. 112. *Crassostrea virginica* (Gmelin)

and a mysterious disease have almost exterminated our native Oysters and now there are only a very few places where they breed fairly freely and self-perpetuate. (Fig. 110.)

Portuguese Oyster *Crassostrea angulata* (Lamarck) (Fig. 111.) A long narrow shell 175 mm from beak to lower margin, with a deeply cupped lower (left) valve, muscle-scar purple, shell often blotched purple. The margins of the valves are often deeply fluted. Often relaid in British waters for fattening but only breeds here exceptionally and is not established. The American Oyster *Crassostrea virginica* (Gmelin) (Fig. 112.) is like the Portuguese oyster but the edges of the valves are smooth, not fluted. Not now relaid here but old valves are sometimes found. With this species were introduced two serious enemies of our oysters, namely the Slipper Limpet (*Crepidula fornicata*) and the American Tingle or Drill (*Urosalpinx cinerea*), both unfortunately now well established in these islands. The Japanese Oyster (*Crassostrea gigas*) (Thunberg) grows to a length of 300 mm so that its identification presents no difficulty. The species is now (1976) being successfully 'farmed' in Strangford Lough, Northern Ireland, and it is planned to introduce it also to Lough Foyle in the same country.

Fan Mussel or Fan Shell

Fan Mussel or Fan shell *Pinna fragilis* (Pennant)   Our largest British shell, sometimes as much as 370 × 200 mm in size. The yellow-brown shell is very brittle. The mollusc lives with its pointed end buried in sandy mud or gravel, attached by a byssus to a small stone or old shell, well beyond LWM and often down to 148 m (80 fm). Local but gregarious where it does occur, on all our coasts. (Fig. 113.)

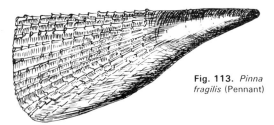

Fig. 113. *Pinna fragilis* (Pennant)

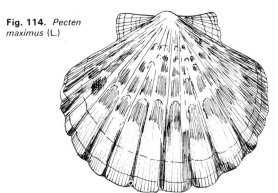

Fig. 114. *Pecten maximus* (L.)

Scallops

Scallops (family Pectinidae) form a colourful and interesting group of bivalves. They have long been used as a source of ornamental motifs, as highly appreciated edible delicacies, and for their beauty of form and colour. In youth most species possess a byssus; some species retain it (e.g., *Chlamys varia*), *Chlamys distorta* becomes cemented by its right (lower) to a stone or old shell and yet other species become free (such as *Chlamys opercularis*). Of the last-mentioned group many can swim by clapping their valves together. Some species have quite elaborate eyes on the tips of the pallial tentacles.

Of the scallops described here the first two species are valued as food and are fished commercially. The third species is also edible but is not exploited commercially.

Great Scallop *Pecten maximus* (L.) (Fig. 114).   Usually 125–150 mm in diam. but exceptionally large specimens have reached over 200 mm. The upper (left) valve is flat, the lower one very convex, and the mollusc lies in a slight hollow on the seabed. Colour red-brown and white. Common and often gregarious, living in banks at depths of a few fathoms and downwards. Sometimes incorrectly called the Pilgrims' Scallop (that worn by Crusaders) but the true Pilgrims' Scallop is the Mediterranean *Pecten jacobaeus* with angular ribs (*P. maximus* has rounded ribs).

Quin or Queen Scallop *Chlamys opercularis* (L.) Usually about 58–62 mm across but may be as much as 80 × 100 mm. Colour, from white (uncommon) to yellow, orange, pink, red, purple, or brown, often marbled or blotched. The 'ears' of the shell are almost equal (in the next species *C. varia* they are noticeably unequal). Very occasionally it may be

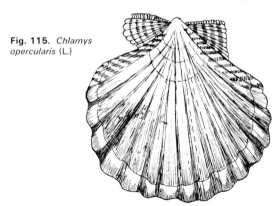

Fig. 115. *Chlamys opercularis* (L.)

taken at LWEST, but is very common in depths of 3–50 m (5–100 fm). It is an excellent swimmer. (Fig. 115.)

Variegated Scallop *Chlamys varia* (L.) (*See* colour plate 6).   Shell with 25–30 ribs, up to 60 mm high. Common, from LWST downwards. Colour as varied as the Queen Scallop; a large broad form (var. *purpurea* Jeffreys) is purple-brown, with about 27 ribs, and measures up to 80 × 75 mm. The scarce *Chlamys nivea* (Macgillivray) is snow-white with 45 ribs; W Scotland only, where it lives moored to seaweeds.

Seven-rayed Scallop *Chlamys septemradiatus* (Müller) (*See* colour plate 6).   A scarce species, with a thin, almost circular shell, red-brown variegated white. There are 3–10 ribs, usually 7. Size, 41 mm high. Widely distributed but nowhere common, in 3–50 m (6–100 fm).

Tiger Scallop *Chlamys tigerina* (Müller) (*See* colour plate 6).   Like a small solid seven-rayed scallop with unequal ears in both valves (in the Seven-rayed Scallop ears are equal in the left valve). Smooth, with fine radiating striae or 3–4 broad ribs. Yellow, brown or purple, often banded or blotched. 24 mm high. All round our coasts, intertidal to 100 m (50 fm), common.

Hunchback Scallop *Chlamys distorta* (da Costa)   The only British scallop which is permanently attached (like an oyster). As the popular name indicates the shape is hunched-up or squashed-looking, though in youth the shells are of the normal scallop shape. Distinguished from young variegated scallops of the same size by the far more

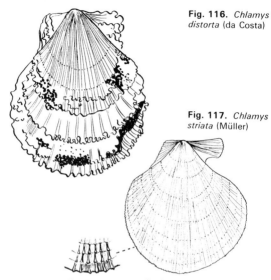

Fig. 116. *Chlamys distorta* (da Costa)

Fig. 117. *Chlamys striata* (Müller)

numerous ribs (up to 70) which are alternately large and small. Colour white, yellow or red-brown, often variegated. Usually about 40 × 35 mm. Common at LWSR and lower, often in *Laminaria* holdfasts. (Fig. 116.)

Ribbed Scallop *Chlamys striata* (Müller) (Fig. 117). A thin fragile shell with a smooth right valve and a left valve with numerous fine prickly ribs. White mottled red-brown, 18 mm high. Fairly common. Do not confuse with the rare *Chlamys furtiva* (Loven) which is smaller (15 mm) and has both valves minutely reticulated.

Little Scallop *Chlamys similis* (Laskey) Small (6 × 7 mm) and very thin, the lower valve much the smaller. No ribs, only fine concentric lines. White mottled red-brown. Widely distributed but not common, between 2–30 fm. (Fig. 118.)

Fig. 118. *Chlamys similis* (Laskey)

File-Shells

The File-shells (family Limidae) are relatives of the scallops. All have white shells and two species (*Lima hians* and *Lima loscombi*) make 'nests' of shell-fragments and gravel, bound together with the mollusc's byssal threads. These 'nests' are not used for breeding purposes but apparently for protection only, and are occupied by groups of file-shells.

File-shell *Lima hians* (Gmelin) (Fig. 119). The largest species (38 × 25 mm) the closed valves gaping at each side. The animal can swim by clapping its valves together as scallops do, showing as it does so long beautiful fringes of scarlet and orange tentacles. Not uncommon as far S as the Isle of Man, from LWM to 25 m (50 fm). In the south it is replaced by the var. *glaciata* (Salis) which is smaller (18 × 10 mm) and has

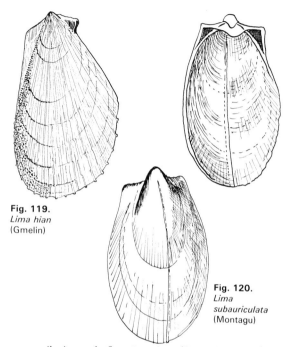

Fig. 119.
Lima hian
(Gmelin)

Fig. 120.
*Lima
subauriculata*
(Montagu)

25–40 ribs instead of 50–60 as in *L. hians*. *Lima loscombi* (Sowerby) is like *hians* but half the size and the closed valves gape at one side only. This species only occasionally makes a nest.

Lima subauriculata (Montagu) (Fig. 120).   An oval shell (not twisted as in the two species just described) with 24 ribs and inside there is a furrow running straight down the centre of each valve from the beak to the lower margin. Size 8 × 3 mm. Fairly common on sandy and gravelly ground. The scarce *Lima sulcata* (Brown) is somewhat similar but twice the size and has 30–40 ribs, and the furrow inside the valves runs obliquely from beak to lower margin, The soft parts are orange and pale pink (milk-white in *subauriculata*).

Astartes and Furrow-Shells

The four British species of *Astarte* have thick shells, white beneath the thick brown periostracum, and mostly with strong concentric ribs. The pallial line is not indented by a sinus.

Common Astarte *Astarte sulcata* (da Costa) (Fig. 121). Rather triangular with 24–40 ribs, the inner margins of the valves thickened and finely crenulated. Size 27 × 30 mm. Generally distributed but rare in the S. The less common *Astarte elliptica* (Brown) is like *A. sulcata* but with smooth margins. Montagu's Astarte (*Astarte montagui* (Dillwyn) is acutely triangular with

Fig. 121.
*Astarte
sulcata* (da
Costa)

105

Fig. 122. *Astarte triangularis* (Montagu)

Fig. 123. *Thyasira flexuosa* (Montagu)

close-set concentric ribs at the umbones, margins smooth with bevelled edges. Size 12 × 12 mm. Fairly common in the N.

Little Astarte *Astarte triangularis* (Montagu) An isosceles triangle in outline, only 3 × 3 mm. Smooth or very slightly striated, margins sometimes smooth and bevelled, sometimes crenulated. Local, gregarious, on all coasts. (Fig. 122.)

Furrow-Shells

Small thin white shells with no 'teeth'; the posterior of the shell is furrowed and there is no sinus in the pallial line.

Common furrow-shell *Thyasira flexuosa* (Montagu) (Fig. 123). The shell is nearly globular, 10 × 9 mm. Common in sandy mud all round Britain. There are three other British species but all are rare and very small.

Lucines

The shells of this group of species are mostly circular in outline, and whitish. There is no sinus in the pallial line.

Loripes lucinalis (Lamarck) A swollen shell with fine concentric striae partly decussated by fine longitudinal striae. Size 15 mm diam. Mainly in the S, at LWM to 40 m (80 fm). (Fig. 124.)

Myrtea spinifera (Montagu) Easily known by the 40–50 fine sharp concentric ridges, their edges forming spines on the dorsal margin. Inside of shell often salmon-coloured. Diam. 20 mm. On nearly all our coasts but local, commoner in the W.

Lucinoma borealis (L.) A swollen shell dull and chalky-looking, with numerous fine concentric ridges. Inside chalky-white with irregular pearly tubercles. Diam. 36 mm. Common, burrowing into sandy mud from LWM to 25 m (50 fm). (Fig. 125.)

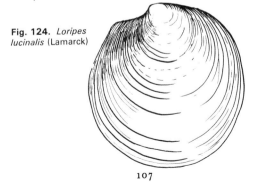

Fig. 124. *Loripes lucinalis* (Lamarck)

Divaricella divaricata (L.)   One of our rarest marine molluscs. The shell is shaped like *Loripes* (p. 107 above) but more swollen and the curious divergent striae at once identify it. Colour, white tinged yellow, diam. 12 mm. Living examples only from Scilly (at LWM); separate valves at Falmouth, Teignmouth and Land's End. (Fig. 126.)

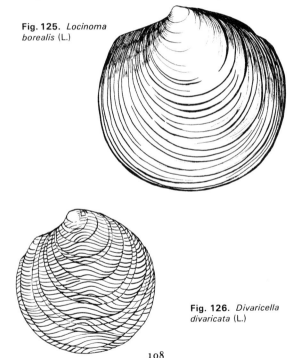

Fig. 125. *Locinoma borealis* (L.)

Fig. 126. *Divaricella divaricata* (L.)

Fig. 127. *Diplodonta rotundata* (Montagu)

Diplodonta rotundata (Montagu) A strong milk-white shell, swollen and glossy, diam. 22 mm. Not uncommon in the S and up the W coast to the Outer Hebrides, S and W Ireland. (Fig. 127.)

The two little bivalves below are both common though often overlooked because of their small size. Rather surprisingly both species can crawl relatively fast with the foot on either hard or soft surfaces. They have no common names.

Fig. 128. *Kellia suborbicularis* (Montagu)

Fig. 129. *Lasaea rubra* (Montagu)

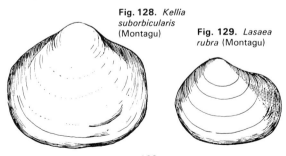

Kellia suborbicularis (Montagu) A thin white globular shell with incurved beaks, 10 × 11 mm. The inside of the shell is silvery. Common, nestling in empty shells or in crevices from LWM downwards. (Fig. 128.)

Lasaea rubra (Montagu) A little transversely oval shell, white flushed crimson or wholly crimson, only 2 × 2·2 mm. Abundant almost everywhere in the empty shells of acorn barnacles (*Balanus*), among the black lichens near HWM and among seaweeds between tidemarks generally. (Fig. 129.)

Coin-Shells

There are half a dozen British species of Coin-shell (*Lepton*) but the two illustrated are the most likely to be encountered. The remaining four species are very tiny (under 2 mm) and scarce. All the coin-shells and their kin are inclined to commensal habits (i.e., necessarily associated with but not actually parasitic upon other animals). Each species of mollusc has a specific host-animal.

Lepton squamosum (Montagu) Unmistakable by reason of its size, a giant among coins-shells, being 8 × 10 mm. Shell is almost flat, snow-white and glossy. The animal lives in the burrows of the prawn *Upogebia* in muddy sand at LWM and below, in the S and W only, rather local. (Fig. 130.)

Lepton nitidum (Turton) A small white oval shell, with a few pittings near the beak (seen only under a good lens); size 2 × 3 mm. Local but not uncommon. (Fig. 131.)

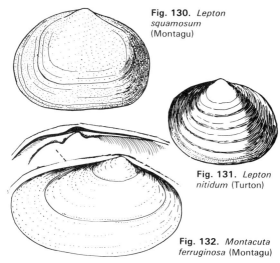

Fig. 130. *Lepton squamosum* (Montagu)

Fig. 131. *Lepton nitidum* (Turton)

Fig. 132. *Montacuta ferruginosa* (Montagu)

Montagu's shell *Montacuta ferruginosa* (Montagu)   A small greyish-white oblong shell usually encrusted with a rusty deposit, 4 × 7 mm. Common in muddy sand, always associated with the burrowing heart-urchin *Echinocardium cordatum*. (Fig. 132.)

Mysella bidentata (Montagu) (Fig. 133).   A small white and rather rhomboidal shell, 4 × 6 mm. Common in muddy gravel and in crevices of old bivalves, associated with the sand-dwelling brittle-star *Acronida brachiata*. Do not confuse with *Montacuta ferruginosa*; although the hinge-line is similar *Mysella* is a much squarer shell, without the rusty deposit.

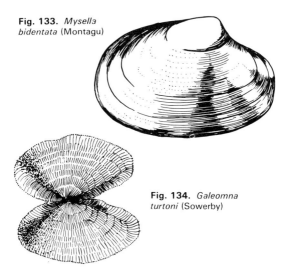

Fig. 133. *Mysella bidentata* (Montagu)

Fig. 134. *Galeomna turtoni* (Sowerby)

Galeomma turtoni (Sowerby)   A thin white shell with numerous delicate ribs, 6 × 11 mm. In life the mollusc appears as shown with the two valves widely opened, forming an almost circular disc. It is sometimes moored by a byssus, sometimes moves about freely. SW and Channel Islands only, from near LWM downwards. (Fig. 134.)

Iceland Cyprina and Heart-Cockle

Iceland Cyprina *Arctica islandica* (L.)   A large thick and heavy shell yellow-white beneath the brown periostracum. Size 100 × 105 mm, occasionally even larger. It burrows shallowly in muddy sand at LWM and beyond to considerable depths. Primarily a northern species its range extends from the White Sea to the Bay of Biscay, and all around our coasts. It was once eaten in Iceland and efforts are now being made to exploit it commercially for food in the USA under the name of 'ocean quahog'. (Fig. 135.)

Heart-Cockle *Glossus humanus* (L.)   Another large species, easily recognized by its incurved and inrolled beaks; the shell is almost spherical and heart-shaped when viewed sideways. Size 100 × 95 mm. The shell is dirty white or fawn beneath the thick brown periostracum. Rather local on muddy ground in 8 m

Fig. 135.
Arctica islandica (L.)

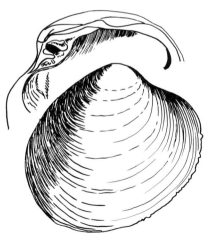

(4 fm) and deeper water, mainly in the SW and in the Irish Sea. (Fig. 136.)

Fig. 136.
*Glossus
humanus* (L.)

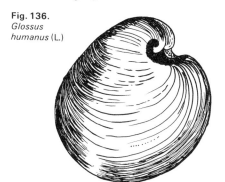

Prickly Cockles and Smooth Cockle

Cockles are well-known molluscs and are represented in Britain by eleven species. The shells are usually globular with thick valves and prominent ribs. The species described on this page are the largest of our cockles.

Prickly Cockle *Cardium echinatum* (L.) (Fig. 137).   Height up to 72 mm, a thick shell with short spines which are connected at their base by a low ridge. There is hardly any posterior gape. The soft parts are yellow-white or pink. Common on all our coasts from 2 fm downwards. The allied *Cardium tuberculatum* (L.) is like the Prickly Cockle but larger (up to 85 mm) and more globular and solid with 21–22 ribs (Prickly Cockle has usually 20). Spines very short and set individually and not connected at the base. Channel Islands and SW at LWEST. The uncommon Spiny Cockle *Cardium aculeatum* (L.) is the largest British cockle, up to 100 mm. The shell is thin but strong and there is a large posterior gape. Soft parts vermilion. In the SW only.

Smooth cockle *Cardium crassum* (Gmelin)   A large shell up to 75 mm and almost smooth, with only a very few faint ribs in the centre of each valve. Cream-colour sometimes mottled red-brown, inside often pinkish. Widely distributed just offshore. (Fig. 138.)

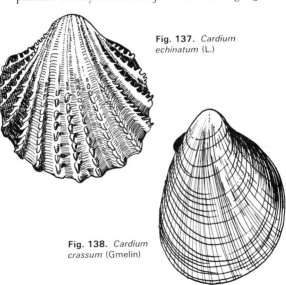

Fig. 137. *Cardium echinatum* (L.)

Fig. 138. *Cardium crassum* (Gmelin)

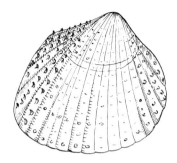

Fig. 139. *Cardium ovale* (Sowerby)

Cockles

The following three cockles are all smaller than the Common Cockle and may be overlooked as being merely young specimens of that species.

Cardium ovale (Sowerby) (Fig. 139). Has 24–26 flattened ribs with tubercles on those at the posterior and transverse blunt plates on the anterior ones. Inside furrowed throughout. Up to 12 mm high. Common on muddy sand around our coasts from 3–111 m (2–60 fm). *Cardium scabrum* (Philippi) is also common, with 24–28 ribs thickly set with small tubercles or arched plates and furrows not extending far inside the valves, 11 mm high.

Angled Cockle *Cardium exiguum* (Gmelin) Strongly angled with 20–21 ribs more or less tubercled, inside not furrowed, 12 mm high. Common from LWM downwards and tolerates low salinities hence sometimes occurs in estuaries. (Fig. 140.)

Common Cockle *Cardium edule* (L.) (Fig. 141). Strongly ribbed, usually about 45 mm but sometimes much larger. Common, living just below the surface from halftide down to LWM in large sandy bays, often in vast numbers, and preyed upon by various seabirds. They are also gathered in large numbers for human consumption. The allied Lamarck's Cockle *Cardium lamarcki* (Reeve) (formerly considered a variety of the Common Cockle) prefers lagoons and similar isolated bodies of brackish water. It differs from *C. edule* in having a tiny ligament only half the length of that of *C. edule,* ribs on posterior hardly developed, and the shell is often produced posteriorly. Inside of shell is generally brown and the shell is thin.

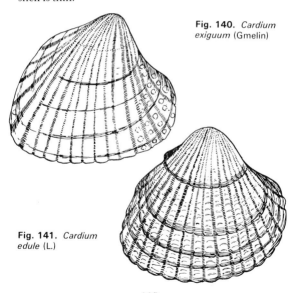

Fig. 140. *Cardium exiguum* (Gmelin)

Fig. 141. *Cardium edule* (L.)

Venus-Shells

The Venus-shells and Carpet-shells form an attractive and often colourful group, with strong shells; there is a deep sinus in the pallial line. There are nineteen species known in British waters; this includes two American introductions now well established here.

Dosinia exoleta (L.) (Fig. 142).   An almost circular shell with numerous flattened concentric laminae, margins bevelled within. Diam. about 50 mm. Colour, white or fawn, sometimes variegated brown or pink. Common, LWM to 80 m (40 fm). The equally common *Dosinia lupina* (L.) is smaller (30 mm) more polished and convex, milk-white, the beaks often pink. Both species of *Dosinia* burrow deeply, *Dosinia exoleta* into muddy gravel, *D. lupina* into sandy mud.

Little Venus *Gafrarium minimum* (Montagu)   Nearly circular with numerous flat broad and concentric ridges. Colour very varied, white, yellow or brown,

Fig. 142. *Dosinia exoleta* (L.)

Fig. 143. *Gafrarium minimum* (Montagu)

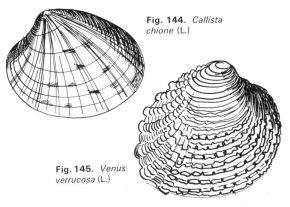

Fig. 144. *Callista chione* (L.)

Fig. 145. *Venus verrucosa* (L.)

often variegated. Size 14 × 15 mm. Common from 7 m (4 fm) downwards. (Fig. 143.)

Smooth Venus *Callista chione* (L.) A large smooth and polished shell, golden-brown with darker rays, often pink-tinged. Young shells have rows of spots instead of rays or sometimes three broad white rays. Adults measure 70 × 75 mm. Burrows shallowly in sand from just below LWM to 130 m (70 fm). SW only, as far north as the Lleyn peninsula North Wales. (Fig. 144.)

Warty Venus *Venus verrucosa* (L.) Easily recognized by the globose shell with warty concentric ridges; young shells look cancellated. Yellow-brown, size 45 × 50 mm. S and W only, not uncommon burrowing shallowly at LWST. (Fig. 145.)

Pale Venus *Venus casina* (L.) Smaller (40 × 45 mm) and much flatter than the Warty Venus, ribs never warty. Shell white or pale yellow beneath the brown periostracum. Common on all our coasts burrowing just offshore. (Fig. 146.)

Oval Venus *Venus ovata* (Pennant) With 40–50 fine ribs radiating from the beak; the ribs are crossed by fine concentric striae so that the ribs are tuberculated. Yellow variegated with red-brown, 13 × 17 mm. Common in 4–185 m (2–100 fm). (Fig. 147.)

Banded Venus *Venus fasciata* (da Costa) With broad concentric ridges. Colour purple, red, pink, yellow or brown, streaked, rayed or blotched, sometimes white. Size 20 × 22 mm. Common in gravel from 4–111 m (2–60 fm), but occasionally found under stones at LWM. (Fig. 148.)

Venus striatula (da Costa) With numerous close-set concentric ribs, crowded at each end. Colour

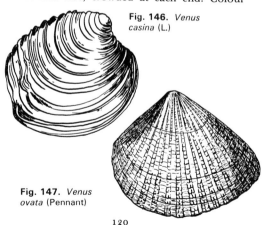

Fig. 146. *Venus casina* (L.)

Fig. 147. *Venus ovata* (Pennant)

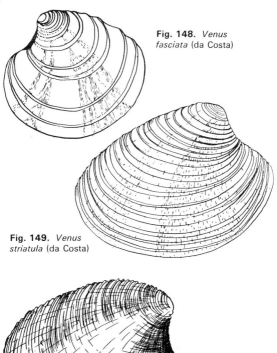

Fig. 148. *Venus fasciata* (da Costa)

Fig. 149. *Venus striatula* (da Costa)

Fig. 150. *Mercenaria mercenaria* (L.)

yellow-white usually with three red-brown rays from the beak. 28 × 32 mm. Very common in sand from about LWM to 55 m (30 fm). (Fig. 149.)

Quahog or Hard-shell Clam *Mercenaria mercenaria* (L.)   A large heavy shell, 75–120 mm across, white or grey, sometimes with brown zigzag markings, inside often stained purple. A North American species introduced experimentally in Devon, Dorset, Essex and Ireland. There are flourishing colonies in the Solent, in Southampton Water and Portsmouth Harbour, but a Humber colony seems to have died out. A much-esteemed edible species. (Fig. 150.)

Carpet-Shells and American Piddock

There are five British species of carpet-shell, forming a well-marked group. Four of the species burrow shallowly, and one prefers rock-crevices.

Golden Carpet-shell *Venerupis aurea* (Gmelin) (*See* colour plate 8).   A glossy golden-yellow shell variegated red-brown or purple, inside often purple or yellow. Size 32 × 37 mm. In rather muddy gravel or mud just below LWM. fairly common but rare in Scotland.

Banded Carpet-shell *Venerupis rhomboides* (Pennant) (*See* colour plate 8).   Rather like the preceding species but larger (up to 50 × 62 mm) and oblong instead of triangular. Ribs hardly marked. Glossy, cream-colour tinged pink, often variegated red-brown. Common, burrowing in gravel at LWM.

Pullet Carpet-shell *Venerupis pullastra* (Montagu) (*See* colour plate 8).   Rhomboidal, *not* glossy, surface finely decussated with concentric ridges at the posterior. Yellowish-white variegated red-brown, size 37 × 42 mm. Common from halftide level downwards, often moored by a byssus. The allied *Venerupis saxatilis* (Fleuriau) looks like a distorted *Venerupis pullastra* being longer, shorter or broader, often abruptly truncate, and the concentric ribs at the posterior at raised and laminar. Lives in rock-crevices, empty piddock borings and such-like habitats. Common between tidemarks.

Crosscut Carpet-shell *Venerupis decussata* (L.) Like the Pullet but almost square in outline, the decussation is much coarser and the posterior is tuberculated. Yellowish marked dark brown, size 45 × 50 mm. In muddy gravel or clay below halftide level, mainly in the S and W, not uncommon. (Fig. 151.)

Fig. 151. *Venerupis decussata* (L.)

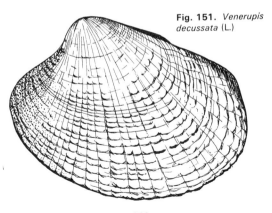

Fig. 152. *Petricola pholadiformis* (Lamarck)

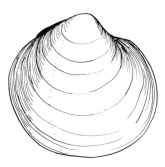

Fig. 153. *Mysia undata* (Pennant)

American Piddock *Petricola pholadiformis* (Lamarck)   Bears a superficial resemblance to the White Piddock (*Barnea candida*) (*see* page 141) but has teeth (two in the right valve, three in the left) whereas *Barnea* has none. A North American species first found in Britain towards the end of the last century, probably introduced with American oysters. Up to 60 mm long. Bores mechanically into clay, chalk, peat and limestone; occurs from Lincolnshire to Dorset and in the Fal (Cornwall). (Fig. 152.)

Mysia undata (Pennant)   A thin chalk-white and fragile shell with a deep sinus in the pallial line. Size 31 × 33 mm. Widely distributed around our coasts in 7–55 m (4–30 fm). (Fig. 153.)

Wedge-Shells and Sunset-Shells

The colourful polished shells of Wedge-shells (*Donax*) are frequent on sandy beaches; the living molluscs burrow near LWM. There are only two British species.

Wedge-shell *Donax vittatus* (da Costa) (Fig. 154). A strong highly-polished shell, yellow, brown or purple, sometimes rayed or banded. About 25 × 37 mm. The inner margins of the valves are crenulated. Common all round our coasts. The related *Donax variegatus* (Gmelin) is flatter, much glossier, and the inner margins are quite smooth. Size 17 × 33 mm. Channel Islands and SW only.

Fig. 154. *Donax vittatus* (da Costa)

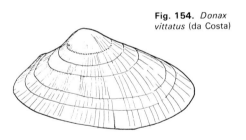

Sunset-shells (*Gari*) are so called from the fancied resemblance of the rays of colour radiating from the beaks to the colouring of sunsets. There are four British species.

Gari depressa (Pennant) The largest species, about 31 × 56 mm, with obscure concentric ridges near the

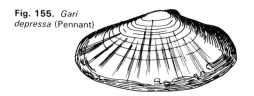

Fig. 155. *Gari depressa* (Pennant)

margins. Colour, yellowish-white rayed purple, inside of valves yellow. Not uncommon, mostly in the S and W. (Fig. 155.)

Gari fervensis (Gmelin) (*See* Colour Plate 7.) With numerous fine concentric ridges, 25 × 45 mm. Very common.

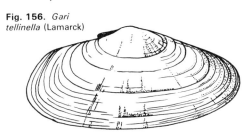

Fig. 156. *Gari tellinella* (Lamarck)

Gari tellinella (Lamarck) (Fig. 156). A glossy little shell (15 × 28 mm), yellow-white tinged purple or flame-colour, rayed or streaked. Common, occasionally at LWM but usually in deeper water. The scarce *Gari costulate* (Turton) is like *G. tellinella* but the posterior slope bears 12–20 sharp ribs. White, heavily marked purple or red.

Tellins

Most Tellins (*Tellina* species) have thin and flattened shells, often brightly coloured. All the species burrow and some are among the commonest shells found cast up on our beaches.

Tellina squalida (Montagu) (*See* colour plate 7). A strong shell, one of the largest of the British species. Usually a rich orange colour but sometimes pink, yellow or fawn. Size 27 × 45 mm. Uncommon on sandy shores, mainly S and W and Ireland.

Thin Tellin *Tellina tenuis* (da Costa) (*See* colour plate 7). Shell thin and semitransparent, pink, yellow or white, 15 × 22 mm. Very common, burrowing in fine sand between tidemarks, often in great numbers.

Baltic Tellin *Macoma balthica* (L.) (*See* colour plate 7). One of the commonest bivalves, colour from white through yellow to crimson. Usually about 18 × 20 mm but sometimes as large as 25 mm long. Lives in mud, muddy sand and muddy gravel between tidemarks, and is tolerant of low salinities so is abundant in many estuaries.

Bean Tellin *Tellina fabula* (Gmelin) (Fig. 157). An oblong fragile shell, pearl-white with a prismatic lustre, size 12 × 20 mm. The right valve only is obliquely striated and this at once distinguishes the species from the Thin Tellin. Very common, burrowing between tidemarks.

Little Tellin *Tellina pygmaea* (Loven) (Fig. 158). Finely striated, the posterior abruptly truncate and rounded. Colour rose, yellow, orange or white,

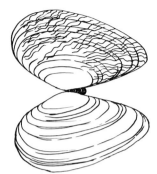

Fig. 157. *Tellina fabula* (Gmelin)

often rayed, size 5 × 9 mm. Fairly frequent, living just offshore. The uncommon *Tellina donacina* (L.) is much larger (20 × 25 mm), usually white with pink rays and an angulated posterior.

Thick Tellin *Tellina crassa* (Pennant) A thick shell with numerous fine concentric ribs, white and pale pink, inside sometimes orange. Size 45 × 52 mm. Common, usually just offshore but occasionally between tidemarks. (Fig. 159.)

Gastrana fragilis (L.) Wedge-shaped with thin concentric ridges crossed by very fine striae. Yellowish-white, size 25 × 37 mm. Very local, S and W coasts. (Fig. 160.)

The group of species described (and three illustrated) here have no English names although they are quite common. All burrow in mud or muddy sand. The shells are thin and flat, white, with a spoon-shaped ligament-pit (the chondrophore) (*see* illustration of *Scrobicularia* hinge-line Fig. 161).

Fig. 158. *Tellina pygmaea* (Loven)

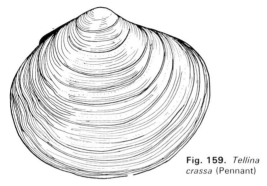

Fig. 159. *Tellina crassa* (Pennant)

Fig. 160. *Gastrana fragilis* (L.)

Scrobicularia plana (da Costa) Much the largest species (37 × 50 mm). The shell is grey-white and the mollusc lives buried in soft mud in estuaries or salt-marsh channels. A very common intertidal species. (Fig. 161.)

Abra alba (W. Wood) (Fig. 162). Shell white, polished and opaline, 12 × 20 mm. Lives at extreme LW, but is usually more abundant in about 5–10 fm. The little *Abra tenuis* (Montagu) is triangular in shape, size 7·5 × 10 mm and lives in brackish-water lagoons and intertidal mud-flats in estuaries. Rather local.

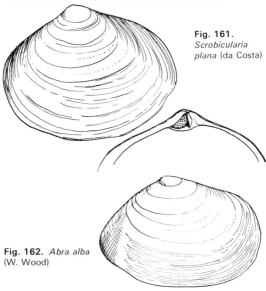

Fig. 161.
Scrobicularia plana (da Costa)

Fig. 162. *Abra alba*
(W. Wood)

Abra prismatica (Montagu) (Fig. 163). Shell very thin and fragile, pearl-white and highly-polished, size 10 × 20 mm. Common in sand at LWM all round our coasts. *Abra nitida* (Müller) is rather like *A. prismatica* but is oval instead of wedge-shaped, 11 × 20 mm. Widely distributed but not common.

Fig. 163. *Abra prismatica* (Montagu)

Pod-Razors and Razor-Shells

The Pod-Razor *Pharus legumen* (L.) A thin yellow-white shell shaped like a bean-pod, 100 mm long. Abundant in large sandy bays as far N as the Clyde and around most of Ireland, living near LWM. (Fig. 164.)

Solecurtus scopula (Turton) (Fig. 165). Yellow-White, compressed in the middle, with 40–50 oblique striae which are absent from the anterior. Size 22·5 × 48 mm. The soft parts (i.e., the 'animal') are bright orange. Occasionally found at LWM in clean gravel but usually lives deeper, down to 30 m (16 fm). Widely distributed but local. The allied *Solecurtus chamasolen* (da Costa) is flatter and larger (25 × 55 mm) and lacks the oblique striae. Both shell and soft parts are white. Uncommon; in thick mud or muddy gravel, S and W.

Fig. 164. *Pharus legumen* (L.)

Fig. 165. *Solecurtus scopula* (Turton)

The Razor-shells (Family Solenidae) all have long, light and razor-shaped shells beautifully adapted to the speed with which these molluscs burrow. Opinions vary as to whether there are five or seven species in our waters; six are described here and four figured.

Cultellus pellucidus (Pennant) The smallest British Razor, a thin little flattened shell, curved, with the hinge near one end. Yellow-white often marked pale pink, length 37 mm. Common. (Fig. 166.)

Ensis ensis (L.) Small and gently curved, the anterior end rounded and both margins curved and

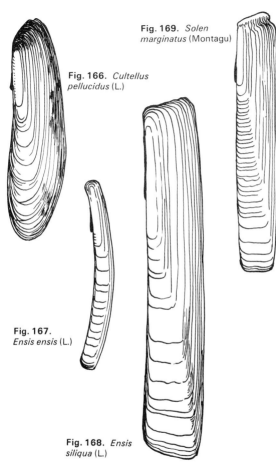

Fig. 166. *Cultellus pellucidus* (L.)

Fig. 169. *Solen marginatus* (Montagu)

Fig. 167. *Ensis ensis* (L.)

Fig. 168. *Ensis siliqua* (L.)

parallel. Length 95 mm. Common in sandy bays. (Fig. 167.) The closely-allied *Ensis phaxoides* (Van Urk) is like *Ensis ensis* but the shell is noticeably tapered at each end. *Ensis arcuatus* (Jeffreys) is curved like *Ensis ensis* but is much larger (up to 150 mm long) and both ends are truncated. Common at LWEST and downwards.

Ensis silique (L.)   The largest Razor-shell we have, up to 220 mm long with both ends abruptly truncated. Common in fine sand at LWM and downwards. (Fig. 168.)

Solen marginatus (Montagu)   Unmistakable because the shell has a deep constriction at the anterior end (as if it had been tied with a string when soft!). Colour yellow-brown or orange, length 125 mm. Rather local, mostly in the S and W, as far north as the Clyde and all round Ireland. (Fig. 169.)

Trough-Shells

All the Trough-shells burrow in sand or mud and all except *Mactra glauca* (*see* page 136) are common. In all the shells the teeth are fairly strong and in the left valve the two cardinal teeth join to form a projection in the shape of an inverted 'V'.

Mactra corallina (L.)   A thin swollen shell, yellow-white or red-brown, often purplish at the beaks. Size 37 × 50 mm. The variety *cinerea* (Montagu) has a rayless shell of grey or cream-colour. Both common in sand at LWEST and lower. Sometimes washed ashore in countless millions after a gale. (Fig. 170.)

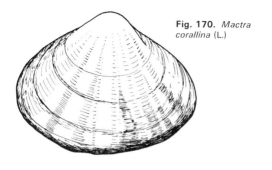

Fig. 170. *Mactra corallina* (L.)

Fig. 171. *Spisula solida* (L.)

In the next three species the lateral teeth are finely serrated—in *Mactra* they are smooth.

Spisula solida (L.) (Fig. 171). A thick strong shell, yellow-white, with a fan-shaped pattern of grooves on the dorsal area; in the next species (*S. elliptica*) this area is smooth. Size 35 × 40 mm. Common about LWM all round our coasts. The allied *Spisula elliptica* (Brown) is smaller (20 × 30 mm), much thinner, and in the left valve the 'V'-shaped teeth reach more than halfway down the hinge-plate (in *S. solida* they reach barely halfway down). Common, always living offshore to about 93 m (50 fm).

Spisula subtruncata (da Costa)   Rather like *S. solida* but is much smaller (about 20 × 27 mm), more convex, and strongly angulated on both sides. Common in sand about LWM. (Fig. 172.)

Mactra glauca (Born)   Like an 'outsize' *Mactra corallina* (size 75 × 100 mm) but the shell is not swollen as in that species. Colour, yellowish-white with brownish rays and a satiny pale-brown periostracum. Channel Islands, where it burrows 50–75 mm deep in coarse sand. It is fairly common in Jersey, rare in Herm and uncommon in Guernsey. It used to be called the 'five-shilling shell' (i.e., 25p.) this being the price then paid by collectors! Single valves have been taken at Hayle on the N Cornish coast. (Fig. 173.)

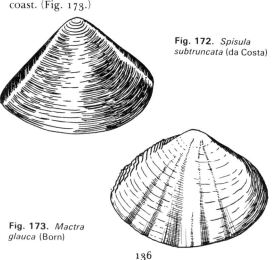

Fig. 172. *Spisula subtruncata* (da Costa)

Fig. 173. *Mactra glauca* (Born)

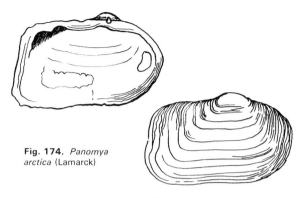

Fig. 174. *Panomya arctica* (Lamarck)

Panomya arctica (Lamarck)   This rare mollusc has no 'common' name but it is allied to the common rock-borer *Hiatella arctica* (*see* page 143). It is a large thick shell, 50 × 75 mm or larger, with a broad furrow in the middle of each valve. It lives deeply buried in muddy gravel in about 55 m (30 fm) in the North Sea—it has also been taken off the W coast of Scotland. (Fig. 174.)

Otter-Shells

The three British Otter-shells (Family Lutrariidae) are large shells, the first-mentioned being the largest and also the most frequently encountered.

Common Otter-shell *Lutraria lutraria* (L.)   A large thin smooth shell up to 73 × 140 mm. White or yellowish beneath the olive-brown periostracum. Common at LWEST, often in soft mud. Occasionally immature specimens are washed ashore in great numbers, presumably due to gales disturbing their habitat. (Fig. 176.)

Lutraria angustior (Philippi) (Fig. 175). Smaller than the Common Otter-shell and a noticeably thicker shell (size 50 × 113 mm), which is narrower from dorsal to ventral margin. The lower margin of the sinus is confluent with the pallial line: in *L. lutraria* they are separate. *L. angustior* lives offshore, mostly in the S and W. Do not confuse with the still smaller *Lutraria magna* (da Costa) (size 43 × 100 mm) which has the posterior slightly upturned. The pallial line as in *L. angustior*.

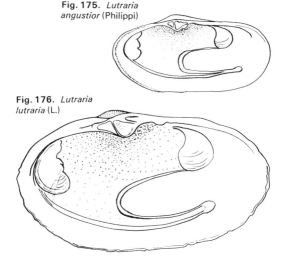

Fig. 175. *Lutraria angustior* (Philippi)

Fig. 176. *Lutraria lutraria* (L.)

Gapers

The two British Gapers are large strong shells, dirty white in colour and unattractive in appearance. The large projecting chondrophore in the left valve distinguishes them from any of the otter-shells (*Lutraria*).

Fig. 177. *Mya arenaria* (L.)

Common gaper *Mya arenaria* (L.) A thick shell, often stained blue-black from the mud in which it lives (it also lives in sand and muddy sand) about LWM. Size about 65 × 100 mm. It tolerates polluted waters and those of low salinity, and is often abundant in estuaries. In waters of low salinity adult specimens are often very small. This is the soft-shell clam so beloved of Americans but not often eaten here. (N.B. the author has eaten it in a chowder and also fried with ham. (Fig. 177.))

Blunt Gaper *Mya truncata* (L.)   Smaller than the

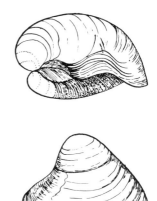

Fig. 178. *Mya truncata* (L.)

Fig. 179. *Corbula gibba* (Olivi)

Common Gaper (only 50 × 65 mm usually) the shell gapes widely at the posterior but hardly at all at the anterior. (Common Gaper gapes at both ends). Common in muddy gravel and sand between tidemarks and below LWM. (Fig. 178.)

Corbula gibba (Olivi) One of our commonest bivalves. A little triangular shell, white or red-brown, the right valve much larger and deeper than the left and overlapping it considerably. About 11 × 14 mm. Common, dredged in shallow water down to great depths; occasionally found at LWEST, muddy sand or gravel. (Fig. 179.)

Piddocks or Pholads

Piddocks (seven British species, one of them rare) are our best-known boring molluscs. They bore into peat, hard clay or rock between tidemarks: two species (*Xylophaga dorsalis* and the rare *Xylophaga praestans*) bore into submerged wood. Boring is mechanical, achieved by the rotation of the shell, the anterior of which bears sharp file-like sculpture. As the burrow is enlarged and as the shells are broadest in front the mollusc is eventually imprisoned. Pholad burrows sometimes cross each other. All the species live between tidemarks and in depths of a few fathoms.

The shells are thin, white, prickly in front, and have a strip-like process (apophysis) projecting from beneath the beak within each valve. In life, some species have accessory plates arranged about the hinge-line but these of course are absent from valves picked up on the shore.

Piddock *Pholas dactylus* (L.) The largest species, about 120 mm long with a row of cells beneath the reflexed umbones. Four accessory plates. The living animal is phosphorescent, glowing with a blue-green light. Mainly in the S and W, and Ireland. (Fig. 180.)

White Piddock *Barnea candida* (L.) (Fig. 181). Half the size of *Pholas* and has no cells but a strong fold instead. One accessory plate. Common. The uncommon Little Piddock *Barnea parva* (Pennant) has an oval shell with many rows of imbricated ridges (the White Piddock has only 25–30 rows), 45 mm long.

Oval Piddock *Zirfaea crispata* (L.) A distinctive

Fig. 180. *Pholas
dactylus* (L.)

Fig. 181. *Barnea
candida* (L.)

Fig. 182. *Zirfaea
crispata* (L.)

Fig. 183. *Xylophaga
dorsalis* (Turton)

shell, to 70 mm long. Common, as far north as Shetland. (Fig. 182.)

Wood Piddock *Xylophaga dorsalis* (Turton) (Fig. 183). Unlike the other piddocks this species bores into submerged wood where it is not uncommon. The globular shell is about 9 × 10 mm. The mollusc lives largely upon the cellulose of the wood into which it bores. The rare *Xylophaga praestans* (Smith) is twice the size and is recorded only from the Northumberland coast.

Rock-Borer

The Rock-Borer *Hiatella arctica* (L.) is responsible for the borings often seen in limestone pebbles upon the beach, and often with the shells of the mollusc still *in situ*. The shell is thick, dull white, with sometimes a spiny double ridge running from the beak to the posterior. Boring is done mechanically by means of the ridges on the shell (in adults these ridges are almost obliterated). Young shells show the ridges clearly and so do specimens which live as 'nestlers', attached by a byssus, within the holdfasts

Fig. 184. *Hiatella arctica* (L.)

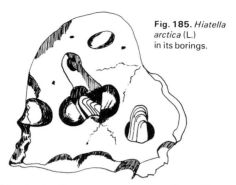

Fig. 185. *Hiatella arctica* (L.) in its borings.

of *Laminaria*. Size up to 15 × 35 mm. The soft parts of the living molluscs are orange-red. (Figs. 184 & 185.)

Ship-Worms

Ship-worms (*Teredo* species) bore into submerged or floating wooden structures and in the days of wooden ships were much dreaded. Ship-worms have a long worm-like body with a small helmet-shaped shell at the anterior end and a pair of shelly paddle-shaped pallets at the posterior. (Pallets are important for identification and should be searched for and kept). Ship-worm borings never cross each other though it is not known how this is managed.

The Ship-worm *Teredo norvagicus* (Spengler) (Fig. 186). Much the largest British species, the shelly tube (which is often thick) measuring up to 300 mm (about 1 foot). Local, but widely distributed in the timbers of piers etc. Another common species *Teredo navalis* (L.) is like a half-sized *T. norvagicus* but the paddle-shaped pallets have a deep cutaway depression at the end instead of the end being flat as in *T. norvagicus*.

Teredo megotara (Forbes & Hanley)   A smaller shell than *Teredo norvagicus* and easily told by the large auricle on the posterior of the shell sticks up above the dorsal line. Common, in drifted timber. (Fig. 187.)

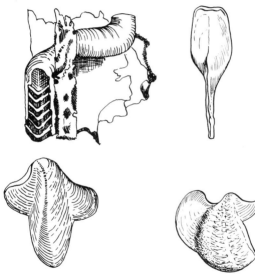

Fig. 186. *Teredo norvagicus* (Spengler) tube, valve and pallet

Fig. 187. *Teredo megotara* (Forbes & Hanley)

Other species sometimes reach our coasts, sometimes even the West Indian *Bankia fimbriatula* (Moll & Roche) with very long pallets (up to 150 mm) composed of many joints with fringed edges.

Lantern-Shells

Lantern-shells have thin fragile shells, usually white, and often difficult to name when beach-worn.

Cochlodesma praetenue (Montagu) Superficially similar to the next species (*Thracia phaseolina*) but differs thus: each valve has a crack on the posterior side of the umbones and a sharp rib on the inside of the valve, running from under the beak towards the posterior. Size 20 × 31 mm. Lives in sand near LWM, rather local. (Fig. 188.)

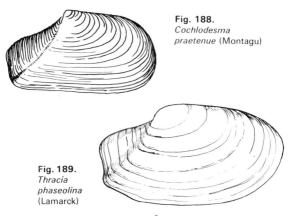

Fig. 188.
Cochlodesma praetenue (Montagu)

Fig. 189.
Thracia phaseolina (Lamarck)

146

Thracia phaseolina (Lamarck) (Fig. 189).   Surface of the white shell is very finely granulated, like finest velvet (seen only under a microscope), periostracum pale-yellow. Size 15 × 27 mm. Common. The closely-allied *Thracia villosiuscula* (Macgillivray) is a thicker and shorter shell, size 15 × 24 mm; texture feels a little rough to the touch (granulations visible under a handlens). Periostracum pale brown. Also common, and the two species sometimes live together.

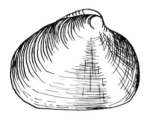

Fig. 190. *Thracia convexa* (W. Wood)

Thracia convexa (W. Wood)   A large (50 × 62 mm), thin sand-coloured shell. Uncommon; burrows deeply in sand and mud offshore. (Fig. 190.)

Thracia pubescens (Montagu)   A large, thin and fragile, sandy-coloured shell up to 60 × 95 mm with a very finely granulated surface. SW England only, in sand and mud below LWM. It has been obtained 'rarely, from trawlers off Plymouth and Penzance' and has also been recorded from Babbacombe Bay, S. Devon. (Fig. 191.)

Lyonsia norwegica (Gmelin)   Very fragile with

numerous rows of fine granulated striae radiating from the beak. Yellowish-white, interior iridescent. Size 18 × 32 mm. Widely distributed but not common. (Fig. 192.)

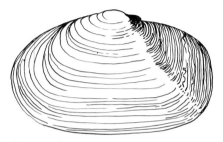

Fig. 191. *Thracia pubescans* (Montagu)

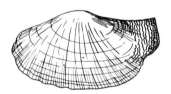

Fig. 192. *Lyonsia norwegica* (Gmelin)

Pandora-Shells

Pandora-shell *Pandora albida* (Röding) (Fig. 193). A pearly shell up to 38 mm long. Lives at LWST and in shallow water, often among sea-grass (*Zostera*), S and W only. The allied *Pandora pinna* (Montagu) is smaller

Fig. 193. *Pandora albida* (Röding)

(10 × 18 mm) and the posterior dorsal line is straight (in *P. albida* it is concave). Widely distributed but uncommon. In both species one valve (the right) is flat and the other (left) is convex and overlaps the former.

Basket-Shells

The Basket-shells (*Cuspidaria* species) are the only carnivorous bivalves and feed on dead crustacea. The shells are thin, fig-shaped and inequilateral with a twisted posterior produced into a 'spout'. All live in depths from 18 m (10 fm) downwards and are uncommon, the first species being the only one likely to be encountered.

Cuspidaria cuspidata (Olivi)   Shell much swollen, white beneath a thick brown periostracum, spout like a long tube about half the length of the whole shell. Size of shell 12 × 20 mm. Has been recorded from NE England, W Scotland and the Firth of Forth. (Fig. 194.)

Cuspidaria abbreviata (Forbes) 'Spout' short and triangular, shell 7·5 × 10 mm. W Scotland and off SW Ireland. (Fig. 195.) Another species is *Cuspidaria costellata* (Deshayes), a fragile iridescent shell, easily known by the 20–30 radiating ribs (the two other species described here have no ribs and are almost smooth), size 6 × 10 mm. Not common, it has been taken off the Isle of Man, W Scotland, Shetland and the Firth of Forth.

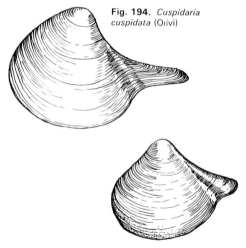

Fig. 194. *Cuspidaria cuspidata* (Olivi)

Fig. 195. *Cuspidaria abbreviata* (Forbes)

FURTHER READING

The following books will be found useful:

For identification:

McMillan, N. F. (1968). *British Shells*. Frederick Warne & Co., London. Describes every British marine mollusc with a shell; many illustrations.

Smith, S. M. (1974). *Key to the British Marine Gastropods*. The Royal Scottish Museum, Edinburgh. One of the *Information Series Natural History. Gratis.*

Tebble, N. (1966). *British Bivalve Seashells. A Handbook for Identification*. British Museum (Natural History). (Reprinted 1976 by the Royal Scottish Museum, Edinburgh). All British bivalves described and illustrated.

Mollusca in general:

Morton, J. E. (1967). *Mollusca*. 4th edn, Hutchinson University Library. (Available in hardback and paperback.)

Books on seashore life in general are numerous; those listed here are recommended and all include a good deal about Mollusca.

Barrett, J. (1974). *Life on the Seashore*. Collins Countryside Series, Collins.

Barrett, J. & Yonge, C. M. (1958). *Collins' Pocket Guide to the Seashore*. Collins.

Clayton, J. M. (1974). *The Living Seashore*, Frederick Warne & Co., London.

Yonge, C. M. (1966). *The Seashore*. Collins New Naturalist Series revised edn, (also available in paperback).

The next two books deal with animals (including Mollusca) of more specialized habitats.

Fraser, J. H. (1962). *Nature Adrift: the Story of Marine Plankton*.

Gotto, R. V. (1969). *Marine Animal Partnerships and other Associations*, English Universities Press. (Includes commensal and parasitic molluscs.)

In addition, the following, now out of print and very expensive, should be consulted. They are available in most large libraries.

Forbes, E. & Hanley, S. (1849–1869). *A History of British Mollusca and their Shells*. 4 Vols.

Jeffreys, J. G. (1862–1869). *British Conchology*. 5 Vols (Vol. 1 deals only with the land and freshwater molluscs).

Sowerby, G. B. (1859 & 1887). *Illustrated Index of British Shells*. 1st edn 1859, 2nd edn 1887.

The following two books are for the serious student:

Fretter, V. & Graham, A. (1962). *British Prosobranch Molluscs their functional anatomy and ecology*. Ray Society: London.

Purchon, R. D. (1968). *The Biology of the Mollusca*. (International Series of Monographs on Pure and Applied Biology). Pergamon Press.

A LAST WORD

For those—and I hope there will be some—who
wish to learn more about living molluscs there are
courses on marine biology held at some Field Study
Centres. For list of Centres and the Courses they
offer write to:

The Council for Nature,
41 Queen's Gate,
LONDON SW7

INDEX

Numbers in bold type are references to figures, those in italics to colour plates

154

155

156

157